TITANIC TOWN
based on the novel by Mary

Anne Devlin was born and brought up in N   ...land. Her
first play, *Ourselves Alone*, was performed to critical acclaim at the
Royal Court in 1985. In 1987 her novel *The Way Paver* was
published by Faber and Faber. Her second stage play, *After Easter*,
was premièred by the Royal Shakespeare Company in Stratford-
upon-Avon in 1994 and transferred to the Barbican in London.
She has written plays for BBC radio and television and also
adapted *Wuthering Heights* for Paramount Pictures (1991). She was
the 1982 winner of the Hennessey Literary Award for Short Stories
and the Samuel Beckett Award for Television Drama. In 1985 she
won the Susan Smith Blackburn Prize. She was co-winner of the
George Devine Award in 1986 for *Ourselves Alone.*

TITANIC TOWN
Anne Devlin

based on the novel by
Mary Costello

faber and faber

First published in 1998
by Faber and Faber Limited
3 Queen Square London WC1N 3AU

Photoset by Parker Typesetting Service, Leicester
Printed in England by Clays Ltd, St Ives plc

Photography by Liam Daniel courtesy of Company Pictures
and Alliance Releasing

A CIP record for this book
is available from the British Library

ISBN 0–571–19675–6

2 4 6 8 10 9 7 5 3 1

CONTENTS

NOTE

This is the shooting script for *Titanic Town*. Some scenes were rearranged in the editing of the film.

Titanic Town

EXT. 139 MUCKROSS. HOUSE. ANDERSONSTOWN. DAY

The family: Bernie, Aidan, Annie, Thomas, Brendan and Sinead are standing facing their new house: 139.

Aidan approaches the door with the keys and Bernie waits patiently. He inserts the key and the lock keeps going round.

> AIDAN
>
> It keeps going round.

A large tawdry version of Miss Piggy is standing in the middle of the small lawn across the road; she is accompanied by an even more bloated figure with a brick, her son Naill.

> PATSY FRENCH
>
> If you want, my Naill will break in for you.

Bernie and Aidan turn, eye the brick.

> BERNIE
>
> No – thank you.

Aidan sighs and looks at the keys.

> AIDAN
>
> Nobody watch. You're making me nervous.

They all turn away.

> ANNIE
> (*voice-over*)
> When I was sixteen my mother became a celebrity.

Another neighbour, Mrs Morris, emerges from the end house.

> MRS MORRIS
>
> Have you come far?

> BERNIE
>
> The Lower Falls. And yourself?

3

MRS MORRIS

Bombay Street. We were burnt out in '69.

ANNIE
(*voice-over*)

We thought we were leaving the Troubles behind; what we didn't know was that they were just beginning.

EXT. LAWN. LATER

Patsy French is looking in the open boxes on the lawn, but only finds books.

Bernie and Annie approach her.

FRENCH

What are they for?

BERNIE

Reading.

FRENCH

You're lucky you've the time.

Bernie removes the book from Mrs French's hand, puts it back in the box and hands the box to Annie.

BERNIE

They belong to my daughter.

FRENCH

She must be awful clever.

BERNIE

She is.

Annie winces and hurries inside.

INT. GIRLS' BEDROOM. DAY

Annie (sixteen) is arranging a display of foreign dolls on her new bookcases. Her books are already in position; Coleridge and Hardy feature. Sinead (nine) is watching.

Mammy says you're too old for dolls.

Annie puts the Spanish dancer down on the shelf next to the Japanese courtesan.

ANNIE
They're not dolls. They're role models.

INT. LIVING-ROOM. SAME DAY. EVENING

Among the cardboard boxes and many outcrops of books in the corner of the room, Nora is reciting; she is surrounded by the helpers from earlier in the day. With Kathleen are her son Colum, Tony and his wife Rosaleen and the family. Uncle James, over from London, is with Lucy, his third wife.

During the recitation, Annie is sitting next to Bernie. Thomas is sitting behind Nora, pulling a face at Annie. Brendan sniggers, Bernie drops her lower lip, revealing clenched teeth. Everyone else is rapt.

NORA
But I will speak their names to my own heart/In the long nights; The little names that were familiar once/Round my dead hearth/Lord, thou art hard on mothers;

Bernie grabs Brendan's head to her breast, nodding vigorously. It proves too much for Thomas who collapses choking on his laughter.

We suffer in their coming and their going; And tho' I grudge them not, I weary, weary of the long sorrow – And yet I have my Joy: My sons were faithful and they fought.

Nora breaks down weeping and is handed a box of tissues by Bernie.

EVERYONE
Yeoh! Aras! Aris!

JAMES
It's a long time since I heard a poem said like that, girl.

KATHLEEN
It'ud take the tear out of a glass eye.

BERNIE
(*to Lucy*)
God love her. She's thinking about her son.

LUCY
Is he dead?

BERNIE
Desy? No, he's in Long Kesh.

KATHLEEN
He's in gaol.

AIDAN
What about a song?

ROSALEEN
Where's Colum? He'll give us a song.

KATHLEEN
Colum – son? Where is he?

Colum appears from the dinette newly refreshed; the door is open, revealing a booze-laden tabletop.

6

COLUM

Right! What'll it be?

KATHLEEN

'Danny Boy'.

COLUM

Oh not bloody 'Danny Boy', moar.

BERNIE
(*to Lucy*)
Our Kathleen's hell for 'Danny Boy'.

Lucy exits to the dinette.

TONY
(*flourishing the tin whistle*)
Sing a rebel song.

NORA

'Roddy McCorley'!

ROSALEEN

'Kevin Barry'!

AIDAN

How about a song where no one gets killed.

Total stunned silence.

COLUM

'The Jug of Punch'!

AIDAN

Why not? If the Brits don't get yous – the drink will.

BERNIE

I hate that song. But it's better than the rifles of the IRA.
Anyway – James's wife is English. You don't want to give
offence.

Lucy comes back from the drinks table in the dinette.

LUCY

I'm not English, Bernie. I'm from Newcastle.

7

BRENDAN
How come Uncle James has had three wives and you've only had one?

AIDAN
He lives in London.

Colum has been negotiating a tune with Uncle James on the fiddle and Cousin Tony on the whistle.

COLUM
(*clears his throat*)
Oh Danny Boy the pipes the pipes are calling . . .

Everyone: cheers of encouragement as the song continues.

EXT. 139 MUCKROSS. NIGHT

His voice swells and the song carries over into the next frame when it ends:

COLUM
(*voice-over*)
Oh Danny Boy I love you so.

A Gordon Highlander is lying in the front lawn with his rifle pointed out over the stone wall. He lifts his head and looks towards the singing: the lit picture window of 139 Muckross Gardens.

CAPTION:
Andersonstown. West Belfast. Early Seventies.

INT. GIRLS' BEDROOM WINDOW. SAME NIGHT

Annie is sitting alone at the upstairs window, between the curtain and the glass, wrapped in a quilt. The house is silent. A helicopter gets closer: the spot in the garden where the soldier was is now empty. She leans forward to see the helicopter searchlights.

BERNIE
(*off*)
Annie? Are you out of bed?

ANNIE
No.

8

There's shooting outside. Stay away from the window.

The helicopter has moved further away, so the sound is fainter. A Gunman is running through the gardens in pursuit of the soldiers on foot patrol. His raised gun is clearly visible. He ducks into the garden in front of the house.

The helicopter returns, searchlights sweeping the gardens. The Gunman moves back into the shadow of the porch. A sharp crack is heard as the Gunman fires.

INT. LANDING. NIGHT

On the landing, Annie finds Thomas (fourteen) and Brendan (twelve). Suddenly Bernie's bedroom door opens – next to Annie's at the front. She is wearing a pair of nylon knickers on her permed hair and an overlong candlewick dressing-gown. She is followed by Aidan.

> BERNIE
>
> I'm going out to him.

> AIDAN
>
> For Christ's sake, woman – wise up!

She tries to push past Thomas who rises up in front of her.

> THOMAS
>
> Where are you going, moar?

> AIDAN
>
> Thomas – don't let her down those stairs!

> BERNIE
>
> He's on my front porch!

> AIDAN
>
> You'll get shot! Where the hell are my clothes?

He flails around in his woolly vest, trying to find something to wear.

> Annie, close your eyes, your father has no trousers on.

> THOMAS
>
> Maybe we should let him in!

9

Bernie marches down the stairs.

> BERNIE

Jesus no. You'll all be lifted.

> AIDAN

It'ud be better than being dead.

> BERNIE

I don't care, I'm not having them shooting at this house.

> AIDAN

Bernie! Don't open that door.

Thomas scrambles after her, followed by Brendan and Annie.

EXT. 139 MUCKROSS GARDENS. PATH. NIGHT

Bernie, standing on the front step.

> BERNIE

Hey you! Wee lad!

The Gunman turns and looks at Bernie.

What the hell do you think you're doing?

Shots from the helicopter land on the pavement.

> GUNMAN

Get in, missus. You'll get hurt.

Bernie advances down the path towards him, candlewick gown flapping.

> BERNIE

If I do it'll be your fault. You'll get us all killed. Now take yourself off and go and shoot at your own door.

Thomas, Brendan and Annie are now standing at the door. Aidan is at the top window in his simmit [woollen vest].

> THOMAS

You haven't a hope in hell firing at a helicopter with that, you know.

GUNMAN

Get the fuck inside or I'll blow your fucking heads off!

Annie plucks at her mother's sleeve.

BERNIE

You insignificant wee bastard!

Bernie marches down the path to lay hold of the Gunman. Annie and Thomas try to hang on to her. The Gunman backs away, waving his gun.

GUNMAN

Don't make me shoot, missus!

BERNIE

You get off this bloody path now or I'll shove that fucking gun up your arse.

He edges down the path.

The helicopter comes back to investigate – sweeping its searchlights over the doorsteps.

The Gunman considers his predicament – between the helicopter and the deep blue Bernie.

GUNMAN

Ah, fuck this!

He leaps over the gate and disappears down the back alley, banging into a metal dustbin. Cats yowling.

The helicopter catches Bernie and her children alone in the spotlight in front of the house.

EXT. MILLTOWN CEMETERY. AFTERNOON

Annie and Maureen, followed by Brigitte, who is smoking, are walking through the cemetery of Celtic crosses and stone angels; in the distance are the school, the bog meadows, the motorway and the factories.

ANNIE

Where are we going? This isn't a short-cut, Brigitte!

BRIGITTE

It is if you know the way.

MAUREEN

A bus would be quicker.

BRIGITTE

I can't afford ten Embassy *and* a bus.

INT. MARY MCCOY'S HAIR SALON. BUSY BEE SHOPS. DAY

Sinead is standing at the window, her hair newly arranged in traditional ringlets.

From the window: Sinead can see Annie, Maureen and Brigitte crossing the road.

SINEAD

Mammy. Annie's here. She's with Brigitte and Maureen.

BERNIE

No wonder she's late.

Sinead removes the plastic cape to reveal an Irish dancing costume.

All right now. Hurry. Come back with a medal.

MARY

Are you not going with her?

BERNIE

She says I put her off.

MARY

Och, she's a wee beauty.

BERNIE

Don't, Mary, be telling her that.

She touches wood.

The door closes, as Sinead, smirking, exits.

EXT. STREET. DAY

Annie, Maureen and Brigitte are passing the shops on the Andersonstown Road. Sinead is walking grandly in front.

ANNIE

Do you think Protestant girls have more sex than Catholics?

MAUREEN

I think when it comes to sex, all mothers are Catholics.

Jimmy Cane, a tall twenty-year-old, is walking towards them; he stops.

CANE

Hi, Brigitte, have you got a light?

Brigitte stops and offers her cigarette.

BRIGITTE

What about you, Jimmy?

Jimmy Cane gives Annie the eye.

Sinead swings round.

SINEAD

We're going to be late!

Annie and Maureen walk on after Sinead.

Brigitte catches up.

ANNIE

Do you know him?

BRIGITTE

Jimmy Cane. He's a mate of our Marion's fiancé.

ANNIE

He's a hateful pig.

BRIGITTE

Oh, you fancy him!

ANNIE

I do not. He's after giving me a dirty look.

INT. PARISH HALL. DAY

Annie, Maureen and Brigitte are watching the three hand-reel finals in St Agnes's Hall.

Sinead is bobbing up and down among the dancers.

> **MAUREEN**
>
> I don't think he was giving you a dirty look.

> **ANNIE**
>
> No?

> **MAUREEN**
>
> It was more of a . . . a sexy look actually.

> **BRIGITTE**
>
> What would you know about it?

> **MAUREEN**
>
> More than you. You only smoke because you think it makes you look sexy. But what you don't know is – you smell like a dirty big ashtray.

> **BRIGITTE**
>
> Fuck off.

> **ANNIE**
>
> What age would you say he was?

> **BRIGITTE**
>
> About twenty-two.

> **ANNIE**
>
> Jesus! Dirty beast. Sure I'm still only a child.

Applause at the end of the dancing.

EXT. BELOW MUCKROSS. DAY

Sinead walking home carrying a large silver cup. Annie trailing gloomily behind.

Suddenly shots are fired.

Sinead standing petrified.

Annie grabs her.

ANNIE

Get down.

Annie pushes Sinead's head down into the grass.

EXT. 139 MUCKROSS. FRONT DOOR. DAY

Bernie rushes out of the house towards a Soldier who is lying in the road.

BERNIE

Holy God!

He is lying on his back and bleeding from his side. He looks terrified. Aidan follows her.

AIDAN

You're all right, son.

Mrs French's door opens; she is followed by Naill.

FRENCH

Did they get him, Aidan? Is he dead?

AIDAN

No. He's been shot in the side.

BERNIE

I'll ring for an ambulance!

Bernie exits indoors.

AIDAN

I'm going to have to lift you on to the pavement where you'll be more comfortable.

Mrs French gives Aidan a strawberry cushion.

FRENCH

Here, stick this under his head.

The Soldier wimpers.

You're bloody lucky the IRA doesn't come back and finish you off, so you are.

More whimpering.

AIDAN

What's your name, son?

LIONEL

Lionel . . . Thirston.

AIDAN

I'm going to take a look at the wound now, Lionel, to see if I can stop the blood.

Aidan opens his jacket, eases his T-shirt up.

Everyone leans forward to look.

NAILL

Yuck!

ANNIE

I think I'm going to be sick.

FRENCH

Jaysus. He's a gonner.

LIONEL

Am I going to die here?

AIDAN

It's not as bad as it looks.

Bernie appears from the house with a towel and gives it to Aidan.

BERNIE

The ambulance is on its way. I'm sorry I couldn't find a better towel for you, son. All my good towels are at the laundry.

Ambulance sirens can be heard in the distance. Annie dashes into the road to wave it down.

LIONEL

I only arrived last week.

AIDAN

Did you? Well, you've had a warm welcome. They'll probably send you home now.

16

LIONEL

I hope so. I'm never coming back.

FRENCH

If you hadn't come in the first place, you wouldn't be lying here now in a pool of your own blood.

The ambulance screeches to a halt.

The Driver and Paramedic hop out and open the doors.

DRIVER

Right, let's get him in!

AIDAN

Aren't you going to bandage the wound first?

PARAMEDIC

Are you mad, mister? This is Apache country.

They hoist Lionel on to a stretcher into the back of the ambulance. He cries out in pain. The doors slam. The ambulance rushes off.

Aidan doubles up, clutching his stomach.

FRENCH

What's wrong, Aidan?

They are all staring at him.

AIDAN

My ulcer's playing me up.

BERNIE

It's all the worry. You just need peace and quiet.

AIDAN

If it was peace and quiet I wanted, I wouldn't have married you.

INT. 139 MUCKROSS. FRONT BEDROOM. LATER

Annie is reading an Evelyn Waugh novel: Vile Bodies.

Sinead is lying in the opposite bed, eyeing the foreign dolls on top of the bookcase.

17

                              SINEAD
If you ever get shot, will you leave me those dolls in your will?

                              ANNIE
No. I want them buried with me.

Annie slides out of bed and goes to the window, getting under the curtain.

Annie's POV: a Gordon Highlander is lying in the front garden. He pops his head up above the short box hedge. It is raining. He is wearing a pompom.

Sinead joins Annie at the window.

                              SINEAD
What's he doing?

                              ANNIE
He's getting very wet.

                              SINEAD
He's crushing the French marigolds.

                              ANNIE
He's wasting his time. The Boys don't come out when it's raining.

INT. FRONT BEDROOM. MORNING

The alarm goes off – seven o'clock.

Radio sounds from the next-door room.

Annie wakes, but remains in bed for a moment.

Then she gets up and opens the curtains.

                              ANNIE
Feck me. Agincourt.

Annie's POV: a great khaki serpent of soldiers, jeeps, Saracens, ferrets, are among the armoured divisions stretching up Muckross and Macroom Gardens. In addition a group of officers are directing operations from the crossroads opposite 139 Muckross.

18

Annie begins to back out of the room.

She turns and opens the door, bursting on to the landing.

INT. LANDING. MORNING

Thomas is standing in front of her.

THOMAS

The Brits have moved in!

Thomas goes downstairs followed by Brendan, who is holding binoculars.

ANNIE

Where were the Boys?

THOMAS

Dunno. They must have been expecting it.

The other bedroom door opens and Bernie appears.

Aidan appears behind her with a radio attached to his ear.

BERNIE

Get dressed! You don't want to be caught in your pyjamas in the middle of a raid.

Aidan follows the boys downstairs, the radio still attached to his ear.

Aidan McPhelimy, you want to put your trousers on. It'll be great if they come to get you and you in your bare arse! . . .

Bernie goes in the girls' bedroom.

Sinead, will you get out of that bed.

INT. LIVING-ROOM. PICTURE WINDOW. MORNING

The family are assembled at the picture window: Brendan with binoculars, Thomas next, then Annie and Sinead, Aidan and Bernie with a mug of tea.

Two Soldiers lead Mr Morris away to an armoured vehicle.

SINEAD

Where are the soldiers taking Bridie's daddy?

BERNIE

Are they arresting him?

AIDAN

What do you think?

BERNIE

But sure he's a quiet wee man. He wouldn't be in anything.

AIDAN

They pick up the quiet ones and see if they can get them to talk about everyone else. It's an old technique.

Bernie opens the door.

They all grab her.

In the name of Jesus, woman – where are you going?

BERNIE

His daughter's handicapped. Sadie Morris needs his wages! I'm going to tell that sergeant.

SINEAD

I'm going with my mammy.

EXT. MUCKROSS GARDENS. MORNING

Bernie takes Sinead by the hand and they walk down the path and cross into the middle of the road – approaching the Soldier in charge of Mr Morris's arrest. The vehicle is open and they can see Mr Morris sitting in the back. He is guarded by a Soldier with a rifle.

BERNIE

Excuse me – where are you taking him? His daughter's deaf and dumb –

SERGEANT

None of your bloody business. Now get back inside! Go on. Hop it!

Bernie turns and walks back to the house.

Two Soldiers follow her.

EXT. MUCKROSS. FRONT DOOR. CONTINUOUS TIME

Aidan is standing at the door shaking his head at her.

> AIDAN
>
> I could've told you.

> BERNIE
>
> I had to try.

Patsy French's door snaps open.

> FRENCH
>
> Do your worst! The British Army has always been great at attacking the defenceless and the down-trodden. We've been fighting yez for eight hundred years. We fought yez at Clontarf. At the Battle of Kinsale and Mullingar.

The Sergeant at the Morris vehicle despatches two more Soldiers to deal with Patsy.

CUT TO:

Bernie and Annie standing at the front door:

When she gets to the Famine call me. She's very good on the Famine.

Bernie exits indoors with Sinead.

FRENCH

The men of ninety-eight fought yez in the fields of Antrim – but we won in the Glens! We shall fight yez in the townlands. And on the streets of Derry, we shall fight yez on the walls and in the Creggan. We shall not fail.

The Soldiers are putting more men into armoured vehicles. Aidan, Thomas and Brendan watching:

AIDAN

Jesus, those fellas they're lifting now are geriatrics.

THOMAS

They must have an old list.

AIDAN

Old? That fella O'Hanlon's not been active since the sinking of the *Titanic*.

The vehicle is now full. The Sergeant sends it away. He walks towards Patsy's house. Four Soldiers precede him.

IST PARA

Excuse me, ma'am.

FRENCH
(*exaggerated politeness*)

Yes. What is it?

IST PARA

We'd like to take a look inside.

FRENCH

And who may I ask are we?

IST PARA

The British Army, ma'am.

FRENCH

And what right have you to search my house. This is Ireland.
A sovereign nation. Not a colony.

1ST PARA

With due respect, ma'am. Ulster is a part of the United
Kingdom.

FRENCH

Ulster, me arse. I do not recognize British jurisdiction in
Ireland.

1ST PARA

Nevertheless we're coming in and we're going to search the
house – with or without your co-operation.

FRENCH

I'm not stopping yez. I've nothing to hide. Wreck the place.
Tear up the floorboards. Terrorize my children. But
remember, I'm admitting you under protest.

1ST PARA

Right!

*Four Paras file into the house, rifles lowered, pushing Naill into the
dustbins.*

*Aidan, Brendan, Thomas, Annie, Sinead and Bernie are standing in
front of their own house; other neighbours are also at front doors.*

BERNIE

Jesus. We'll be next. Away up quick, Annie, and make the
beds.

Annie thumps upstairs.

ANNIE

Why is it always me?

*Paratroopers begin to emerge from Patsy's house with placards and
flags.*

BERNIE

Where's her man these days?

AIDAN

He's gone on the run.

BERNIE

Sure he's not in anything. The IRA wouldn't have him. He's a drunk.

AIDAN

He's gone on the run from her.

Patsy returns to address the neighbourhood again.

FRENCH

They think they have pacified Ireland. They think they have purchased the half of us and intimidated the other half.

Everyone up and down Muckross is mouthing the words with Patsy.

They think they have foreseen everything, but the fools, the fools. They have left us our Fenian dead, and while Ireland holds those graves, Ireland unfree shall never be at peace.

Aidan and Bernie on the step.

AIDAN

Holy God! She got that all right.

BERNIE

I don't care if she did or not. She's letting the whole street down in front of them.

AIDAN

Who cares – it's only the British Army.

BERNIE

I care – there is such a thing as dignified resistance.

A Lanky Para appears from another Saracen.

LANKY PARA

Search, sir?

Aidan steps back.

AIDAN

Sure, why not?

Four Paras, led by the Lanky Para, file into the house.

INT. MUCKROSS. BATHROOM. DAY

Two Soldiers glance into Bernie's toilet.

INT. GIRLS' BEDROOM. DAY

One of two Soldiers gets down and lifts up the frilled valance on Annie's bed and looks underneath, watched by Bernie and Annie.

BERNIE

Tut. Tut. Would you look at the dust under your bed.

Annie gives her mother a withering glance.

EXT. 139 MUCKROSS. DAY

As the search party of four Paras depart the house, another troop carrier arrives and several Paras pour out; they come straight to Aidan. Bernie and Annie are too frozen to move.

Which of you is Ay Dan Mac Feelme?

AIDAN

That's me.

BERNIE

What do you want him for?

CORPORAL

If we could just have you over here, please.

They move Aidan into place against the wall. Thomas and Brendan come tumbling out of the house.

2ND PARA

Against this wall.

3RD PARA

Clear a space.

The other Paras clear a space on either side of Aidan.

Bernie is open-mouthed, her eyes full of tears.

BERNIE

Aidan?

ANNIE

Daddy?

Patsy French comes running down her path.

FRENCH

What are they going to do to you, Aidan?

AIDAN

I think they're going to take my photo actually, Patsy.

A camera is visible for the first time.

3RD PARA

Don't smile, mate.

FRENCH

Do! You're in your own country.

Aidan bursts out laughing and the photo is taken.

> BERNIE

What are you going to do with that?

> 3RD PARA

It's for our files.

> BERNIE

You mean he's a suspect?

> CORPORAL

It's just routine.

> SINEAD
> *(off)*

Daddy.

Sinead comes out of the house carrying a rifle.

Excuse me.

> AIDAN

Sinead, put the gun down.

> 1ST SOLDIER

She's got a gun.

The Soldiers turn; all rifles click into firing positions trained on Sinead.

> AIDAN

Put the gun down, Sinead.

> BERNIE

Holy mother of God!

> 2ND SOLDIER

Drop it! Drop the gun!

> SINEAD

You left your rifle behind.

Lanky Para owns up.

> LANKY PARA

Oops. Better not forget that.

Visible release of tension as he reclaims it.

The Soldiers begin to move away; the family move towards the house.

A shot rings out: sounds of glass imploding. Terrible screams rent the air. Everybody panics.

The Soldier hops into a Saracen, slams the door and it drives off very fast. This Saracen is followed by another.

Bernie runs up the road.

> AIDAN

Bernie, get back here!

> ANNIE

Mammy, wait!

Annie runs after her.

EXT. UPPER MUCKROSS. DAY

Bernie and Annie join Bridie and Mrs Morris who are looking opposite the bend in the road: a bike in a garden.

A picture window is broken. The venetian blinds are half hanging down.

A line of Soldiers wait in disarray beyond the house.

At the top of the path nearest them is a tall fair schoolgirl – Nuala Curran (fourteen). Her face is creased with laughter.

> ANNIE

Why is she laughing?

> BERNIE

She's not laughing, she's crying, love.

> NUALA

Vicious evil murdering bastard. You didn't have to do that!

> BERNIE

What happened, Sadie?

SADIE

I think they shot someone.

Mrs Gilroy runs down from the top of the road to join them.

MRS GILROY

I'm after hearing that Eileen Curran got shot in the face with a rubber bullet. She was opening her window.

Bernie and Mrs Morris, Bridie and Annie and Mrs Gilroy all walk up slowly to where Mrs Brennan is standing opposite the Curran house.

MRS BRENNAN

I saw the one that did it. It was a skittery big get with sandy hair and a wee moustache. Oh he's not here now. The bugger disappeared right after.

MRS GILROY

They got him out for fear the people would lynch him.

MRS BRENNAN

I seen the one who did it and I'm not afraid to say.

A Soldier walks towards the women.

1ST PARA

Inside please. On the double.

BERNIE

Why? So you can shoot more of us, like you shot that poor woman!

Annie and Mrs Gilroy grab Bernie either side and turn her away.

1ST PARA

Get inside, or you'll get the same bloody thing!

The women – Bernie, Annie, Mrs Morris and Bridie, Mrs Gilroy, Mrs Brennan – move away quickly.

BERNIE

I can't believe he said that.

MRS GILROY

Walk slowly, girl. Don't run.

They walk calmly down to their houses, watched by the line of Soldiers behind them.

INT. MUCKROSS LIVING-ROOM. DAY

Bernie follows Annie into the room – to find Thomas, Brendan and Sinead are gathered around Aidan, who is sprawled out unconscious on the floor.

Bernie gasps.

> SINEAD
>
> He says his stomach was hurting him.

> BERNIE
>
> Has anyone called an ambulance?

INT. MARY MCCOY'S HAIRDRESSERS. DAY

Mary McCoy is putting finishing touches to Mrs Brennan's hair.

> MARY
>
> First she wanted it all black but he didn't like it. Then she wanted it with a silver streak but he thought red would be better. When she came back a fourth time I refused. Says I, woman dear, leave your hair alone and change your husband.

Bernie arrives puffing and panting with Brendan.

> BERNIE
>
> Can I leave Brendan with you 'til I get back from the hospital?

> MARY
>
> Surely. He can come to the butcher's with me . . . Sit down and get your breath back.

> BERNIE
>
> I can't. I've still my messages to do.

She glances at the clock.

> MARY
>
> Bernie, you need to take it easy, you know – or you'll end up in the same place as Aidan.

He'll not hold on to that job now. And with me out of work
as well –

MARY

Something will turn up – it always does.

Brendan looks uncomfortable.

Sit down, Brendan. Go on, love. I won't be long.

INT. BUTCHER'S. DAY

Brendan's POV: knives are being sharpened, one against the other.

The Butcher in a stained apron is waiting, he has fat red fingers.

MARY

Oh and I'll have six lamb loin chops for now. And keep a leg
over for Saturday.

BUTCHER

I've no loin. Only shoulder.

MARY

That'll do rightly.

EXT. STREET. DAY

*Mrs McCoy, in a check coat, turns into the street with Brendan sucking
a candy lolly.*

Shots ring out.

Soldiers return the fire.

More shots.

Mrs McCoy falls.

*Brendan walks on, then stops. He turns to look for Mrs McCoy: he sees
a piece of red meat lying open in stained brown paper.*

*He looks at the clump of lamb chops and the spilled meat roll, then he
follows the trail to the fallen body of the owner.*

A Woman comes up and puts a green coat over Mrs McCoy.

A Second Woman joins them, crosses herself and kneels beside the body.

> BERNIE
> (*off*)

Brendan?

Bernie is standing in the street looking at Brendan. She suddenly catches sight of what he is looking at:

Marymotheragod.

> BRENDAN

Is she cold, mammy?

> BERNIE

No, son. She's dead.

> 1ST WOMAN

Do you know who she is?

> BERNIE

Yes. She was my bridesmaid.

Pull back from Bernie and Brendan and the other Women kneeling and

33

standing around Mrs McCoy's body. Relentless clack of army helicopters overhead.

INT. DOUBLE-DECKER BUS. FALLS ROAD. DAY

Annie is sitting behind the Driver of the bus.

She appears to be alone on the bus; apart from one other Passenger, Dino, a young man of twenty-four, who is sitting at the back of the bus. Suddenly he moves up to sit behind her.

> DINO
> (*leaning over to speak to Annie*)
> Excuse me – do you know –

They are startled by the smashing of glass as someone aims a hatchet at the bus windows.

The bus shudders to a halt with a screech of brakes.

All the windows get smashed by a gang of Youths with hurley sticks.

EXT. FALLS ROAD. DAY

The Driver and Conductor flee towards the pub doors; the Youths begin

smashing the bus windows while another Youth tries to drive the bus into a position to block the road.

As the Driver hammers on the closed door of the public house, Annie and Dino follow. The Publican lets them in.

INT. PUB. NIGHT

Annie, Dino, the Driver, the Conductor and the Publican are in the bar.

> DRIVER
> (*on the telephone in the background*)
> We just lost another bus . . . Top of the Falls . . . where else?

Dino dips the cloth in the water and touches his temple, but fails to find the scratch.

> ANNIE
> Och, give us that here.

Annie dabs the scratch.

Dino flinches, takes a swig of brandy.

> Sorry.

> DINO
> This isn't necessary, it's only a scratch.

> ANNIE
> There might be glass in it.

> DINO
> (*taking her hand away from his face*)
> Look, I'm the doctor here, I should know.

Annie drops the cloth immediately.

> ANNIE
> You're a doctor?

> DINO
> Yes.

ANNIE

If there's anything I hate it's a doctor.

DINO

Well, I haven't qualified yet. I still have exams.

ANNIE

My daddy's had an ulcer for years and the doctor told him it was the drink that was doing it . . . He's been a teetotaller all his life.

Annie says this downing brandy.

All doctors want is to put you under the knife.

DINO

I also sell ice cream.

ANNIE

Ice cream? That's much better.

DINO
(*clinking glasses*)

Your good health.

ANNIE

Aye. No more doctors.

Dino notices she likes the brandy.

DINO
(*calling out*)

Could we have another?

INT. THE RVH HOSPITAL. NIGHT

Bernie, sitting by Aidan's bed, is accompanied by Tony and Rosaleen.

TONY

It was that stupid bollocks MacCormac shot Mary McCoy.

BERNIE

I was told it was the Army – not the IRA!

TONY

They had to say that.

36

AIDAN

So what'll they do with him?

TONY

They've set up an inquiry – you know. He'll have to be
disciplined.

BERNIE

Disciplined? Am I on my own here in finding this offensive?

AIDAN

Calm down.

BERNIE

Don't tell me to calm down. Some insignificant wee fucker
has just shot Mary McCoy in front of my son! And you know
what makes it worse? I was relieved that it was her – and not
my Brendan.

Bernie starts to cry.

EXT. PUB. FALLS ROAD. NIGHT

*Dino and Annie are emerging from the pub, they pass the burnt-out
shell of the hijacked bus.*

DINO

How are you feeling?

ANNIE

Em – well, I'd be all right if the corner of the pavement would
stay down . . . Oops . . . It's done it again. Did you see that?

DINO

I can't see anything without my glasses to be honest . . .
(*looking at the burnt-out bus*)
Jesus Christ! . . . You should have told me you've never had
brandy before.

ANNIE

Brandy? I've never had a drink in my life!

EXT. HOSPITAL CAR PARK. NIGHT

Bernie is getting into Tony's car after Rosaleen.

> BERNIE
> Why didn't they own up! Instead of blaming the Brits.

> ROSALEEN
> Because the Brits don't own up!

> BERNIE
> They'll lose the support of the people, Tony.

EXT. CASEMENT PARK/ANDERSONSTOWN ROAD. NIGHT

Dino stops at a bay-windowed house with a high hedge.

> DINO
> Wait right here – and then I'll walk you home.

> ANNIE
> Is this where you live?

> DINO
> No. I've got to drop off my laundry.

Annie looking at the front of the house.

> ANNIE
> It doesn't look like a laundrette.

> DINO
> That's what my sister says.

INT. TONY'S CAR. NIGHT

Bernie is passing Casement Park as Dino leaves the house with Annie.

> BERNIE
> That's another thing. Where were they when Mrs Curran was shot?

> TONY
> They're fighting a guerrilla war, you don't expect them to –

Bernie stares hard at Annie and Dino.

                    BERNIE
Stop the car! Stop the car!

                    TONY
Why, what's wrong?

He slows.

                    BERNIE
I've just seen our Annie with a boy.

He speeds up again.

                    TONY
For Christ's sake, Bernie. I thought the SAS were behind us.

EXT. ANDERSONSTOWN ROAD. MUCKROSS. NIGHT

*Annie and Dino are turning into Lower Muckross: they come upon
Youths with hurley sticks removing a driver from an ice-cream van. He
gets out with his hands in the air and runs away.*

*A Youth with a red scarf tied like a band around his forehead begins
distributing boxes of chocolate flake to the surrounding kids.*

                    ANNIE
Do you have any Neapolitan?

                    HIJACK YOUTH
Are you blind? This is Mr Whippy!

Annie shrugs.

They walk on.

Annie spies Tony's car.

                    ANNIE
Flip me. The wee woman's back. I'd better go.

                    DINO
Why don't we meet when you're sober and I have my glasses
fixed.

                    ANNIE
Okay. But we might not like each other.

39

Bernie, Tony and Rosaleen are in the living-room with Sinead.

> BERNIE
>
> You can't guarantee it won't happen again. As long as you have shooting in broad daylight, and children coming home from school, and women shopping.

> SINEAD
>
> I hid in the bushes.

They look at Sinead.

> BERNIE
>
> Go and help Thomas put the shopping away, like a good girl.

Sinead goes.

> Do you have any Valium, Rosaleen?

> ROSALEEN
>
> Here.

Bernie swallows and drinks water at the same time.

> BERNIE
>
> All we need is to get the shooting retimetabled.

> TONY
>
> I agree with you.

> BERNIE
>
> Can't you talk to somebody?

> ROSALEEN
>
> He already has.

> TONY
>
> There's a meeting tomorrow. It's just for the women from the estate. Why don't you go along to that.

> BERNIE
>
> Me? Rosaleen knows more about this than I do.

TONY

Aye but if Rosaleen says anything it'll look as if I'm getting involved.

ROSALEEN

I'll go with you.

INT. DINETTE. NIGHT

Sinead unpacking and eating Weetabix at the same time. Thomas pouring tea. Brendan also raiding the groceries.

SINEAD

Is Cousin Tony one of the Boys?

THOMAS

Nah. He's just their political adviser.

Annie comes in via the back door, wearing a doleful look.

She knows.

ANNIE

Jesus.

Annie blesses herself before she opens the door to the living-room.

INT. LIVING-ROOM. NIGHT

Rosaleen and Tony are facing her; Bernie has her back to the door.

BERNIE

All I want is a peaceful life for my children.

Bernie catches sight of Annie.

I'm going to kill you, wee girl.

ANNIE

Why? What's wrong?

BERNIE

Have you completely lost your mind? Mary McCoy's lying dead tonight, and Eileen Curran has lost half her face! And what is our bold Annie doing running around chasing boys.

ANNIE

I have no idea what you're talking about, mother.

BERNIE

Don't cheek me. I saw you at Casement with my own eyes.

TONY

Easy on, Bernie.

BERNIE

I left you looking after this house and this family.

ANNIE

They aren't my children. They're yours!

Annie exits.

ROSALEEN

So what are you going to do?

BERNIE

I'll go to the meeting.

INT. ASSEMBLY HALL. CBS SCHOOL. MORNING

Bernie, Rosaleen, Mrs Gilroy and her sister, Mrs Brennan arrive in the hall. Priests, Nuns and some middle-aged well-dressed Residents are present. A group of Journalists led by a woman carrying a camera on her shoulder rush forward.

IST JOURNALIST

Are you from the estate?

2ND JOURNALIST

What do you think of the Provos?

3RD JOURNALIST

Are you the Women for Peace group?

The camera light is switched on, and a microphone thrust into Bernie's hand.

BERNIE

No.

2ND JOURNALIST

You don't support peace?

The light is blinding Bernie.

BERNIE

Yes. We do want peace . . . But has anyone noticed the level
of Army activity on this estate recently?

The Journalists look uncomfortable and switch off the camera light.

1ST JOURNALIST

That's fine thanks.

2ND JOURNALIST

Dead on. Thank you.

*A commotion as the doors open again: this time a parade of Women in
suits arrive. They are physically taller than Bernie and her friends. The
Journalists rush off towards them.*

ROSALEEN

Well, they're not from Andytown.

GILROY

They're not from the same planet!

MRS BRENNAN

They look like Unionists to me.

The Women in suits are being led up to the platform.

BERNIE

They look like they're going to do all the talking.

Rosaleen starts to propel Bernie forward, aided by the others.

ROSALEEN

Here, Bernie, get you up there.

*Polite applause is dying down, the Chairwoman is approaching the
microphone.*

BERNIE

I can't. I'm sorry.

43

MRS LOCKHART

Thank you . . . Thank you on behalf of the South Belfast
Women's Institute Women for Peace Group – bit of a
mouthful that – for the invitation to speak to you. My name is
Alison Lockhart.

CUT TO: *Rosaleen.*

ROSALEEN

What did I tell you – they're Protestants.

CUT BACK TO: *the platform:*

MRS LOCKHART

Before I open the meeting, I'd like to remind you that only
women can stand together and show the way. Only by
reaching a fuller, deeper understanding of each other's needs
can we come together peacefully as one community.

Rosaleen pushes Bernie.

ROSALEEN

Go on, Bernie!

Excuse me, but the point of this meeting – I live on this estate
– is that we can't have shooting during the daytime.

The Reporters move in.

The audience is intent, lots of shushing, cries to be quiet.

MRS LOCKHART

Would you like to come up on to the platform, and state your
name.

*Bernie goes up towards the group at the platform. A Man in a grey
overcoat helps make way for her and then whispers to her as she gets on
to the platform.*

MAN IN GREY OVERCOAT

I warn you – don't mention the IRA.

Bernie looks around – he fades into the crowd.

Rosaleen and the others find seats.

BERNIE

I'm Bernie McPhelimy . . . ah . . . We need to be very
practical . . . First of all the people outside should be allowed
in to speak.

The microphone shrieks.

VOICES
(*off*)

Speak up!

MRS LOCKHART

Mrs McPhelimy. We do have an agenda – and intend to take
one issue at a time.

BERNIE

There is only one issue for the people of this area and that's to
get the shooting stopped.

MRS LOCKHART

I think we need to look at the broader picture first: I think our
first priority is to find links between our two communities.

Deirdre Gorman rises to her feet from the floor of the hall, directly behind Rosaleen.

A distant roar of hammering at the doors can be heard off.

DEIRDRE

I'd like to support what Bernie McPhelimy has just said.

MRS LOCKHART

Would you please identify yourself.

DEIRDRE

Deirdre Gorman . . . You see we have a local problem here. It may not be the same as your problem –

The Protesters burst in, led by Mrs French.

FRENCH AND CHORUS

No peace without Justice! No peace without Justice! No peace without Justice!

Deirdre, standing in the middle of the hall, comes face to face with Patsy French.

Bernie is now on her feet, as are the rest of the platform Women.

FRENCH

You fucking backsliding traitors! One bit of trouble and you join the opposition!

BERNIE

Pull yourself together, Patsy. You're not performing for the troops now.

FRENCH

You're fucking cowardly bitches, so yous are.

DEIRDRE

Here, you watch your dirty mouth!

FRENCH

And you wash your dirty neck!

DEIRDRE

Oh, who have we got here, Madam Defarge?

Mrs Lockhart raps the table.

> MRS LOCKHART

Ladies! Please can we deal with this calmly and address your remarks through the chair.

> FRENCH
> (*to Lockhart*)

You can shut your bake for a start!

Mrs Lockhart shrinks.

Bernie leaves the platform and comes down into the hall to face Patsy.

> BERNIE

I'm just as angry as you are! Mary McCoy was a friend of mine.

> DEIRDRE

And she wasn't shot by the Army!

> FRENCH

Eileen Curran was blinded by the fucking Army!

> BERNIE

I want the Army activity curtailed as much as the IRA's!

> FRENCH

The British Army don't live in Andersonstown. The IRA do. They're just defending their homes. They have a right –

> BERNIE

We live here too! Or we're trying to.

> FRENCH
> (*pointing to Mrs Lockhart*)

Those women don't live here! Come on, girls!

Patsy turns to her supporters who begin a chant.

> FRENCH AND CHORUS

No peace without justice! No peace without justice!

They pelt the platform with eggs.

EXT. GIRLS' SECONDARY SCHOOL GATES. DAY

Annie, Maureen and Brigitte are leaving school. Annie is carrying a small sports bag.

The only vehicle in sight is an ice-cream van: Morelli's Italian Ice Cream. The ice-cream van driver lowers his newspaper and smiles.

> BRIGITTE
> So did he kiss you then?

> ANNIE
> No but he talked to me.

> BRIGITTE
> Nothing's like being kissed.

EXT. BELFAST CITY DOCKS. DAY

Annie and Dino are walking past the harbour at the Harland & Wolff Shipyards. Two giant cranes dominate.

> DINO
> That's where they built the *Titanic*. They painted No Pope Here on the side.

ANNIE

Lucky Pope!

INT. DOCKS. PUBLIC HOUSE. DAY

Annie, Dino, Brian and Fergus are drinking in a docklands bar.

FERGUS

Will you have another one?

ANNIE/DINO

Yes/No!

Dino looks at Annie and then at Fergus.

DINO

She's not used to it.

The TV news is turned up.

ANNIE

I've only had two glasses.

BERNIE
(on TV)

I think this is disgraceful behaviour so it is.

Annie starts, frozen stiff.

It's not setting a very good example to the young ones!

Annie is convinced now that Bernie is behind her.

1ST REPORTER
(on TV)

How do you think the IRA will react?

2ND REPORTER
(on TV)

Is this a move to get the IRA out of Andersonstown?

Annie slowly turns to look at the TV screen, high in the corner of the bar.

CUT TO: *Close-up on Bernie on a black-and-white screen; Patsy French is in the background.*

49

BERNIE
(*on TV*)

Ach well, no – not exactly. I mean, how could I do that? We want to get them to stop shooting during the day when the children are around, and civilians. After all, Mary McCoy is dead. And I'm not about to be intimidated into keeping quiet by anyone.

RESUME:

Annie is sinking back into the walls of the pub.

CUT TO:

Bernie in full glint of the sun.

BERNIE
(*on TV*)

It's terrible when you can't even speak out on your own estate.

FRENCH
(*on TV*)

Traitors!

BERNIE
(*on TV*)

We have a right to bring our children up in peace.

Bernie's name is designated in white lettering below her picture.

RESUME:

Annie, Dino, Fergus and Brian turn away from the set.

DINO

Bloody Peace Women. Their brains are out the windows.

Annie looks under pressure.

BRIAN

Aye, you can't have peace at the expense of freedom or justice.

DINO

She's the same name as you.

50

ANNIE

She's my ma.

FERGUS

She's your ma!

They laugh.

BRIAN

Slante!

ALL

Slante.

INT. RVH CORRIDOR. NIGHT

Aidan on a phone to Bernie in the corridor.

AIDAN

Am I seeing things, Bernie, were you not just on the six o'clock news – attacking the IRA? . . .

CUT TO: *Bernie on the dinette phone.*

BERNIE

Those journalists twist everything.

CUT TO: *Aidan.*

AIDAN

You only had to say no. You said not exactly.

CUT TO: *Bernie.*

BERNIE

I didn't mean it was only the IRA was the problem. I blamed the Army too, you know.

CUT TO: *Aidan.*

AIDAN

You didn't say anything about the Army.

CUT TO: *Bernie.*

> BERNIE

I was edited.

CUT TO: *Aidan.*

> AIDAN

Jesus, Bernie, I hope this is only a bad dream.

Sweat is pouring down Aidan's face.

Jesus.

He passes two pregnant women in dressing-gowns on the long empty hospital corridor.

> 1ST PREGNANT WOMEN

There was a head where the foot should be. It just turned around at the last minute.

> 2ND PREGNANT WOMAN

Aye. Girls do that.

INT. VAN. LOWER MUCKROSS. PATH. NIGHT

Dino drives up and stops the car.

She touches the door handle.

> ANNIE

I have to go. Thanks for a great evening.

> DINO

Hang on.

He leans over as if to open the door, pressing against her breasts.

He brings his face and lips very close to hers.

Annie doesn't move.

I'm going to kiss you.

He kisses her.

A Saracen drives past, the Soldiers all cheer.

Finally they part.

52

Then Annie, dazed, gets out of the car. Walks quickly away.

He waits, then turns on the engine.

INT. 139 MUCKROSS. HALL/LANDING. NIGHT

Annie quietly lets herself into the front hall, closes the front door.

Thomas is standing at the kitchen door eating a piece of toast.

> THOMAS
>
> Moar was on TV.

> ANNIE
>
> I know.

> THOMAS
>
> She's gone to another meeting.

Flying at him.

> ANNIE
>
> Christ, Thomas! Are you mad! Why did you let her out?

> THOMAS
>
> What do you want me to do, board up the door?

> ANNIE
>
> Frig it – that woman's always screwing up my life!

Sounds of a key turning in the lock.

> THOMAS
>
> Here she comes!

Bernie comes in looking pleased.

> ANNIE
>
> What's going on, mother?

> BERNIE
>
> There's been a coup.

> THOMAS
>
> A coo?

BERNIE

We formed a peace group.

INT. KITCHEN. MORNING

Bernie is cheerfully pouring milk on to cornflakes and dishing out toast. Annie and Thomas look gloomy; Brendan and Sinead are blissfully unaware.

BERNIE

We're just going on TV to make clear we're a group of concerned residents trying to make the streets safer for our children . . .

ANNIE

It's not what it looks like. It looks anti-IRA instead of pro-peace.

THOMAS

Did you hear what Mrs French called yous?

BERNIE

Och, nobody takes any notice of her.

Bernie swallows Valium.

INT. CLOAKROOM. DAY

Annie is with Maureen.

ANNIE

I don't know if I can handle this. I don't mean handle. I mean cope.

MAUREEN

You mean handle.

ANNIE

My shoes are missing. Oh, Christ! I didn't sleep a wink.

Brigitte arrives in the cloakroom, with another Schoolgirl.

Annie looks expectantly towards Brigitte.

ANNIE

He kissed me. He really kissed me.

Brigitte stares in disbelief.

BRIGITTE

You can talk about that after what's happened?

ANNIE

Why, what's happened?

Nuala Nolan steps forward to support Brigitte.

NUALA

Your mother has no right to bring middle-class Protestants into Andytown!

ANNIE

But she didn't!

BRIGITTE

She let the Catholics down in front of everybody.

Brigitte walks quickly out of the cloakroom followed by Nuala.

Annie looks dismayed.

INT. DINETTE TABLE. MUCKROSS. DAY

Annie has seated Bernie at the kitchen table; she is leaning over Bernie's shoulder, Thomas is at the other shoulder. Bernie is reading a piece of exercise paper.

BERNIE

Who wrote this?

ANNIE

I did.

THOMAS

I helped her.

ANNIE

If you say that – you'll not get into trouble.

55

INT. TV STUDIO. DAY

Bernie and Deirdre Gorman, seated side by side, face an Interviewer.
Bernie has been too heavily made up. Her hair is stiffly glued.

INTERVIEWER

Now – Mrs McPhelimy. You were critical of the IRA.

BERNIE

I said . . .

She glances down at the exercise sheet, reads:

'We need the IRA to defend us. And we need them to
maintain law and order in Andersonstown, because we can't
rely on the RUC.'

INTERVIEWER

So now you're being critical of the police – what do you want?

BERNIE

I'm saying:
(*reads*)
'Since the formation of the Provisionals the crime level on the
estate has dropped.'

INTERVIEWER

The Provisional IRA shot Mrs McCoy.

BERNIE

Yes. The IRA shot Mrs McCoy, I condemn them for that.
What I want is to get them to reschedule the shooting.

INTERVIEWER

Oh, so you don't mind if they shoot people – it's just a matter
of the time of day.

BERNIE

Don't put words into my mouth!

INTERVIEWER

It's okay – we'll cut that out. What is your immediate plan of
action, Mrs Gorman?

DEIRDRE

We intend to seek a meeting with the IRA in Andersonstown to ask for their co-operation.

INTERVIEWER

Do you think you'll succeed?

DEIRDRE

If they value the support of the people.

INTERVIEWER

Do you speak for the people of Andersonstown, Mrs McPhelimy?

BERNIE

Very definitely.

EXT. CBS PLAYING FIELDS. DAY

Thomas is playing hurley; he is watching the ball coming towards him. He backs away to meet the ball with his flat stick when another player's flat stick lands on the side of his face. He falls over from the blow.

(*off*)
Tell your ma to keep her fucking mouth shut.

A whistle goes.

INT. CLASSROOM. DAY

Miss Savage is writing on the board. Annie arrives and goes to her desk.

MISS SAVAGE
Annie, you're late – O Romeo, Romeo! wherefore art thou?

Annie slowly opens the desk. Her papers, shoes on top, are covered in dog shit. She lifts a shoe out and examines it, then she closes the lid. Several heads turn.

Misunderstood because Shakespeare didn't mean where – he meant why? Girls! Girls!

INT. RVH. MEN'S WARD. DAY

Bernie is seated next to Aidan's bed. The curtains are drawn round them.

BERNIE
It all started over a wee meeting at the school.

Bernie begins to sob.

AIDAN
So why didn't you pull out when you saw what was happening?

BERNIE
I meant to – but I was trying to correct the first wrong impression on TV that I was blaming the IRA for everything.

AIDAN
Bernie, you went on TV again to claim you represent the people of Andersonstown against the IRA – that's a big mistake. You're not elected, and you're not the IRA. You can't win this.

BERNIE

I don't want to win. I just want a decent life for my kids.

AIDAN

Your kids. Oh holy Jesus, Bernie, I was afraid to mention
your kids. I thought you'd forgotten them.

BERNIE

If you shout at me, I'm going home. The Bishop of Down
and Connor is right behind us.

AIDAN

Fuck the bishop! You tell the bishop from me that I would prefer
he was standing in front of you, considering where we live.

A Nurse pulls the curtain back sharply.

NURSE

Blood pressure, Mr McPhelimy.

Bernie gets up to leave.

AIDAN
(*calmly*)
You better get Tony to put up some bullet-proof glass inside
the front door.

INT. ANNIE'S BEDROOM. NIGHT

Annie is asleep.

Footsteps on the path.

A stone strikes the window, somewhere.

Annie opens her eyes.

INT. LANDING. NIGHT

*Annie opens her bedroom door to find Thomas and Bernie already on
the landing.*

They indicate that she should be quiet. All three listen.

*A larger object finds its target; suddenly there is a terrific sound of glass
breaking.*

                              THOMAS
    Fuck. Kristalnacht!

                              BERNIE
    That's our front window.

                              THOMAS
    Nobody move.

All three rush downstairs, led by Thomas.

INT. MUCKROSS. LIVING-ROOM. NIGHT

Bernie opens the living-room door. The dining-room table is full of glass.

Naill French's brick is on it.

EXT. MUCKROSS GARDEN. NIGHT

Thomas opens the front door and looks out. The path is clear; the shadowy street is empty. A lone dog is barking at him

INT. RADIO STUDIO. DAY

Bernie is being interviewed on Ulster Today. *She is wearing headphones and sitting opposite a male interviewer.*

                              BERNIE
    I came here to make clear that I won't be bullied into silence
    by my neighbours.

                          INTERVIEWER
    You had your windows broken –

                              BERNIE
    Yes. But I didn't come here to complain about that. I came
    here to issue a challenge to the IRA to talk to me.

                          INTERVIEWER
    What would you say to the IRA if you met them?

                              BERNIE
    I am raising four children in what looks like the front line of a
    battle zone. We're hostages, so we are. We're being used as

hostages. It does seem a cowardly way to run a campaign to use young families as cover. That has got to stop.

> INTERVIEWER
>
> Do you think you'll succeed in getting them to listen to you?

> BERNIE
>
> I'd like to see if they possess the kind of courage it takes to make peace. I'm throwing down the gauntlet, here today. We're the people you're so fond of saying you represent. We're the people you say you exist to defend. What is there to lose in talking to me? You know where to find me: talk to me. Talk to me.

EXT. QUEEN'S UNIVERSITY, BELFAST. DAY

Annie is mesmerized drinking in the span of the building before her.

Dino arrives.

> DINO
>
> You got away from the dragon.

> ANNE
>
> Thanks for ringing.

DINO

I got her on the phone the first time so I pretended I was selling double-glazing. The trouble was she was very interested – what is it?

Annie turns to look at Queen's again.

ANNIE

We used to come over here every Sunday on our way to the Botanics. And my mother used to stand me on the wall and say, 'That's Queen's University, Annie, that's where you're goin' when you grow up.'

DINO

Is that her ambition or yours?

Annie laughs.

Dino goes off.

Come on.

ANNIE

Where are we going?

INT. ULSTER MUSEUM AND ART GALLERY. NEXT TO QUEEN'S. DAY

Close-up on an oil painting called The Twelfth of July, *Portadown, 1928, by Sir John Lavery.*

DINO
(*off*)

I was about sixteen. July. It was very hot. And I was selling ice cream in Portrush, when Paisley turned up to address this big meeting. I'd never heard him speak before. So I stayed on to listen.

PULL BACK *to reveal:*

Annie and Dino are standing in front of the painting in the gallery overlooking the Botanic Gardens.

DINO

Well, he's a powerful orator. And he kept going on about
Romanism – and the evils of Rome rule. Morelli's Italian Ice
Cream was written all over the van; and it occurred to me that
sooner or later they were going to make the connection
between Italy and Rome. No use pretending I was Mr
Whippy.

ANNIE

So what did you do?

DINO

That's when I turned on the chimes . . . The crowd parted
like the Red Sea. Nobody could hear a word . . .

Annie laughs.

They watch each other.

ANNIE

Stop looking at me like that.

DINO

I wish I could go to a room with you and lie down.

ANNIE

I have to go soon.

*Dino gazes at Annie who is completely unaware of how much he wants
her at that moment.*

INT. LIVING-ROOM. NIGHT

*Annie is dressed as Pooh-Bah; Thomas is mending a Bohran. Bernie is
pinning alterations to the costume.*

ANNIE

Jesus Christ!

BERNIE

What's the matter with you?

ANNIE

Coconut snowballs! . . . Mother, just once could you please
allow the situation the gravity it deserves.

63

BERNIE

Would tinned salmon be better maybe?

THOMAS

Ma, do you have any idea how many years you'd get in Armagh if the Army raided this house while your visitors were here.

BERNIE

Don't be giving me heart failure.

ANNIE

Do we even know if this is a friendly visit?

BERNIE

I don't know what it is – hold still! I just got a message that they were coming.

ANNIE

But why are you on your own? Where's your peace group now? Who else got their windows broken? Who else's kids –

Pause as Thomas gives Annie a warning look.

BERNIE

Who else's kids? What ?

THOMAS

Live on this estate –

The phone goes once.

She jabs Annie with the needle.

ANNIE

Owh!

BERNIE

Sorry . . . That's the signal.

She starts clearing the sewing things away.

THOMAS

How long after the phone goes?

Three loud raps at the door.

BERNIE

They're here.

Thomas bolts for the dinette.

Annie goes to the door.

Bernie sits down to compose herself. Then thinks better of it and stands up.

The living-room door opens as Annie shows in a very small man, Finbar, between two larger Satellites, who behave as if they were invisible. Annie is wearing her Mikado *costume throughout. Bernie begins shaking hands with Finbar.*

FINBAR

Glad to meet you, Mrs McPhelimy. Just call me Finbar.

BERNIE

Sit down. Take the weight off your feet. This is my daughter Annie.

Finbar looks at Annie.

She's doing an opera at school, *The Mikado.*

Finbar begins to whistle a few bars from the arrival of The Mikado.

ANNIE

That's the one.

FINBAR

Who are you? The Emperor?

ANNIE

No. I'm Pooh-Bah. The Lord High Everything Else.

FINBAR

Sure that's a lovely part.

ANNIE

I would like to have played a female role.

FINBAR

Maybe next time.

Yeah.

They sit.

BERNIE

I hope you don't mind if Annie stays.

FINBAR

Not at all.

BERNIE

I was around, you know, when Mrs McCoy was shot.

FINBAR

A terrible business.

BERNIE

Aye well it is – and it's the kids, you know. My Brendan was with her. He's at that age when all his friends are out stoning the soldiers. I said to him last week when there was a riot on, you put one foot across that door and I'll break both your two legs. And there's that one over the road. Her son's a hood. She's the bane of my life.

FINBAR

Could we have a wee word there?

The Satellite nods.

Bernie looks at Annie.

Finbar pops a Gelusil into his mouth.

BERNIE

Do you have an ulcer?

FINBAR

Aye.

BERNIE

That's what's wrong with my husband, you know. An ulcer.

FINBAR

So I understand.

BERNIE

The doctor says it's stress. All the shootings and the riots and
so on.

FINBAR

It's the same with me. I'm an oul worrier. Not for myself. It's
those young fellas. I'm responsible for them, they've never
known a normal life.

The door bursts open and Thomas appears with a tea tray.

BERNIE

Terrible. I'd never any son of mine out to die for Ireland!

Thomas looks at the company, puts the tray down, nods and retreats.

Anyway, he's got too much homework.

FINBAR

And with all these raids, they never get a moment's peace.
Now if we could get these raids stopped. There'd be no call
for half the shooting.

BERNIE

Could you not organize a truce?

FINBAR

The British would refuse to meet us.

Annie offers him a plate of Mikado *biscuits.*

He shakes his head.

BERNIE

Will you have a dry biscuit?

FINBAR

No, I'll have a wee bun.

He bites into a coconut snowball.

INT. SCHOOL MUSIC ROOM. DAY

*Annie comes into the music room, several Girls, including Brigitte, are
gathered around the piano practising bars from* The Mikado*: 'Three*

Pretty Maids from School'. They stop mid-phrase. Silence. Annie walks across the room to get her bag.

Someone plays 'The Death March' on the piano: everyone laughs.

INT. LIVING-ROOM. DAY

Annie, Sinead, Brendan and Thomas are watching a cowboy film on TV.

Bernie comes into the room, glances into the fireplace mirror. Her hair is bigger, her lipstick brighter and her foundation more suitable for TV studio lights than the living-room.

> ACTOR
> (*on TV*)
> Those Apaches are getting bolder every day, Bruce. I thought they were going to follow you into camp.

All look up at Bernie, who is fastening earrings, unaware of the attention. Aidan comes in from the dinette as Bernie swallows Valium.

> AIDAN
> I'd go easy on the Valium, Bernie. You need to keep your wits about you.

> BERNIE
> You should have stayed in hospital.

A loud burst of gunfire makes Bernie jump.

> Turn that bloody TV off! Is it any wonder I'm up to high doh.

> AIDAN
> You're off for talks with the IRA and you're giving out about them watching a cowboy film – Jesus, that's rare!

> BERNIE
> It's a question of setting an example. I'm trying to take the gun out of politics here.

> AIDAN
> If you want to set a better example don't go!

68

Rapid knock at the window.

They all freeze.

BERNIE

That's our Nora – she always raps the window. Go on, let her in.

Thomas goes to the door.

Nora comes into the room carrying a parcel, followed by Thomas.

NORA

I'm not staying.

BERNIE

What's this?

NORA

It's from our Desy.

Bernie takes a hand-tooled leather bag out of the paper.

He made it in the Kesh. It's for you.

Bernie has tears in her eyes.

BERNIE

I didn't know Desy was so talented.

NORA

Neither did he. He's off the drink and learning Irish. Best thing that ever happened to him. I'm not in too big a hurry to get those boys out of gaol.

Aidan snorts.

Hi, Aidan. I'm glad to see you looking so well.

Aidan smiles weakly.

Bernie is switching the contents from one handbag to the other.

She finds a brown envelope with twenty pounds in the new bag.

It'll hansel your bag. It's from me.

She nods at Aidan.

It's just to help you out.

BERNIE

You shouldn't.

The phone rings once.

Everybody freezes.

NORA

Was that the phone?

EVERYBODY

No.

Bernie glances at the window: a car has appeared silently.

BERNIE

Stay and have a cup of tea, Nora. There's Annie will make it for you.

She looks at Aidan; then kisses Sinead and Brendan and Thomas.

Well, I'm off . . . Don't anyone wish me luck.

Brendan, scowling, rubs the lipstick off the side of his face.

AIDAN

Ask them who orchestrated the brick through your window.

Aidan nods at the brick which is prominently displayed on the mantelpiece.

BERNIE

Who orchestrated the brick?

Bernie looks in disbelief at the brick.

Aidan raises his eyebrows.

EXT. CAR. DAY

Bernie is getting into a car in the rain. A Minder is holding open the door. Deirdre and the Driver are already in the car.

INT. MUCKROSS. LIVING-ROOM. DAY

All the kids are peering out of the window at Bernie getting into the car.

THOMAS

He opened the door for her.

ANNIE

She'll like that.

Aidan snorts.

Nora looks uncertain.

Annie leaves the room and comes back with her coat on.

AIDAN

Where are you off to?

ANNIE

I have an opera rehearsal.

She lets herself out.

INT. CAR. DAY

Deirdre Gorman and Bernie are seated in the back of a car; the Driver and Minder in the front.

DEIRDRE

Are you not going to blindfold us?

DRIVER

I don't think that will be necessary.

BERNIE

Are you from Cork?

DRIVER

It would be wise not to ask questions, missus, under the circumstances.

BERNIE

I'm sorry. I wasn't being nosy. It's just that I went to Cork on my honeymoon.

DEIRDRE

I'd rather they blindfolded us, you know.

The car passes an Army Footpatrol.

The Soldiers all stare into the car.

DRIVER

Keep calm.

EXT. ANDERSONSTOWN ROAD. DAY

An ice-cream van with Dino and Annie, her head on his shoulder, passes the car with Bernie and Deirdre going in opposite direction.

INT. SITTING-ROOM. SAFE HOUSE. DAY

Bernie and Deirdre are sitting side by side on a sofa, a clock is ticking. It is still light outside the windows which are heavily veiled in white lace with large drapes tied back on either side.

BERNIE

Lovely room.

DEIRDRE

Lovely.

BERNIE

I like them curtains.

She gets up to examine the pattern.

DEIRDRE

What happened to your man?

BERNIE

Damask . . . I think we're the only ones here.

DEIRDRE

Bernie, would you keep away from the window, you're
making me nervous.

BERNIE

Why?

DEIRDRE

The curtains are pulled back . . .

BERNIE

What are you saying?

DEIRDRE

A machine-gun attack through that window would be a very
easy way of getting rid of two troublesome females.

Bernie walks back to the sofa.

BERNIE

They'd start a war!

DEIRDRE

That would make a change.

*After a pause, Bernie starts getting her rosary out of her bag. Crosses
herself and begins a decade.*

Deirdre follows her example.

BERNIE

Mary of Perpetual Soccer.

DEIRDRE

Have mercy on us.

A whining door slowly opens towards them; they freeze, look up and find the Driver.

DRIVER

There's been a change of plan.

EXT. TYRELLA BEACH. NEWCASTLE. BLINK

Annie, Dino and their friends, including Fergus, Brian and Emer, are gathered around a fire on the sunlit beach smoking, drinking and talking.

INT. CAR. BLINK

The car is now being driven in blinding rain on a country road. Bernie stares at her watch. It is two hours since they began. Suddenly the car swerves as it does a complete U-turn; Deirdre and Bernie are thrown around in it.

BERNIE

Are we getting home tonight?

DRIVER

We're nearly there.

EXT. BEACH. BLINK

Annie and Dino are now dancing on the beach.

EXT. LANE. NIGHT

Bernie, Deirdre and the Driver are crunching up a lane to the back of an old house.

They enter the house through the rear kitchen.

INT. DINING-ROOM. SAFE HOUSE. NIGHT

Bernie and Deirdre are led into a smoke-filled room by the Driver. A ring of five men, including Finbar, rise from a circular table to meet Bernie and Deirdre.

DEIRDRE

Och, would you look at that!

BERNIE

We're not far away from home, Finbar.

FINBAR

How did you know that?

DEIRDRE

Different room. Same curtains.

(*pause*)

Everyone looks at the window. The damask curtains are drawn.

If that's an example of your security it's laughable.

They move to the table.

The man beside Bernie smiles.

CAHIR

Hello, Bernie.

BERNIE

Och, Cahir!

FINBAR

You two know each other?

BERNIE

The Waves of Tory.

CAHIR

The Walls of Limerick.

BERNIE

We were Irish dancing partners.

CAHIR

Champions.

The Driver laughs.

FINBAR

Well, we're a bit short of time and there's quite a lot to get
through –

Bernie takes a brick out of her handbag and puts it on the table.

They all stare at her.

> **BERNIE**
> It's the brick that came through my window. I want to know, did you conduct it or what?

> **FINBAR**
> Did we what?

> **BERNIE**
> Did you . . . orchestrate it?

> **CAHIR**
> Did someone suggest that we did?

> **DEIRDRE**
> We criticized you and Bernie's windows got broken – the suspicion is there without anyone suggesting it. It's a simple yes or no.

> **FINBAR**
> Mrs McPhelimy – those people were not acting on the authority of the Republican Movement. We have already given a warning there – but if you're not satisfied –

No. No. I am. I am satisfied.

EXT. BEACH. NIGHT

Annie and Dino are lying in the sand dunes a little way back from the party. Dino kisses her.

ANNIE

Not here.

DINO

Not here, not anywhere.

ANNIE

Then not anywhere . . . I can't help it.

He gets up and begins to undress.

DINO

Okay.

He strips off his shirt and then his trousers.

ANNIE

What are you doing?

DINO

I'm going swimming.

He is now perfectly naked; he holds his hand out to her.

She is still fully clothed.

She lets her strap off her shoulders. Drops her dress and reveals her swimming costume underneath.

He has his back to the sea and is facing her.

She steps towards him.

Fergus appears at the top of the sand dune and has a view of Dino.

FERGUS

I see naked bodies!

CENTER: DINO

Fuck off, Fergus!

Fergus disappears.

CENTER: *(taking her hand)*

Come on, McPhelimy.

They race off down to the water.

INT. SAFE HOUSE. NIGHT

As before: Finbar, Cahir and three Others with Bernie and Deirdre.

CENTER: CAHIR

The Army are gettin' very fly. They've stopped their night patrols and are saturating the place during the day. Obviously we can't let them do that.

CENTER: BERNIE

It's a housing estate, Cahir – it's not a battlefield!

CENTER: DRIVER

Do you have a strategy yourself?

CENTER: BERNIE

No.

CENTER: FINBAR

Well, it might be an idea if your group was to go to Mr Whittington and explain our position. We would certainly be prepared to work something out about the shooting in this area.

INT. STRANMILLIS FLAT. LATER. NIGHT

Dino, having closed the door on his friends, is standing with his back to it, watching Annie standing alone in the middle of the room. Annie has finally understood the meaning of the gaze. She smiles encouragement.

CENTER: ANNIE

That's the door I have to go through.

CENTER: DINO

I know. That's why I'm standing here.

78

She moves towards him, lifting her skirt invitingly.

He circles her and places her back to the door.

They begin to make love against the door.

Someone knocks at the door.

They are arrested.

The knocking continues.

> DINO

Who is it?

> BRIAN
> (*off*)

Emer forgot her handbag.

> DINO

Come back tomorrow!

> BRIAN
> (*off*)

Dino – her keys are in her handbag.

> DINO

Fuck's sake!

In a towering rage Dino grabs Emer's bag off the chair and opens the door, shoves the bag into Brian's face. Suppressed laughter from the hallway.

When he turns around Annie is picking up her coat.

> ANNIE

I didn't realize it was so late.

> DINO

Listen, the flat'll be empty on Friday. Take the afternoon off school.

INT. MAIN BEDROOM. MUCKROSS. NIGHT

Aidan in bed. Bernie at her dressing-table, putting her knickers on her head and swallowing Valium.

BERNIE

What could go wrong?

AIDAN

The only reason the British Government will talk to you is because the IRA sent you. You have no authority.

BERNIE

I give myself the authority – as a mother!

AIDAN

Do you want my advice? Be careful what you agree to. Somebody always shoots the messenger!

BERNIE

Why are you so negative all the time? You didn't used to be.

AIDAN

Do you want to come to bed, Bernie? You never seem to want to come to bed.

She looks at him.

BERNIE

You're always so ill.

INT. CAR. UPPER BELMOT ROAD. STORMONT PARK. DAY

Deirdre has her head in a map. Bernie is clutching the steering-wheel and staring ahead.

BERNIE

I wish we'd let Father Clancy drive us.

DEIRDRE

So do I. You're still in third.

BERNIE

Why don't you drive?

DEIRDRE

I'm better at navigating.

BERNIE

Is Stormont not on that map, Deirdre?

Deirdre glances out to the side, touches Bernie's arm: they have arrived at the black and gold gates of Stormont.

Bernie turns the little car into the drive and stops at the police checkpoint.

They sit for a moment at the bottom of the drive, defying the imperial grandeur of the portland stone building on the hill ahead of them.

A Policeman – one of several – moves towards the car.

> DEIRDRE
> We're going to see – what's his name? George Washington.

The Policeman shakes his head.

> BERNIE
> Whittington!

Bernie hands her a letter.

> DEIRDRE
> George Whittington – sorry.

Having glanced at the letter, the Policeman waves on the car. They drive up to Stormont and climb the steps.

INT. STRANMILLIS FLAT. DAY

Annie opens the door of the flat with a Yale key.

She looks at the clock. Two-thirty exactly.

She sits; the bed creaks.

INT. THE GREAT ROOM. STORMONT. DAY

Bernie and Deirdre are shown into the Great Room: classical cornices, bare-arsed cherubs and gilt-framed oil paintings decorate the walls – among the pictures of ships is one of the Titanic.

Whittington is waiting amid a show of grey-suited male power: the heads of the business, Army and civil administration.

> WHITTINGTON
> I've been looking forward to meeting you both so very much. Welcome.

They all shake hands.

Have you met my assistant, Jeremy Immonger?

Bernie and Deirdre shake hands with the civil servant as well.

IMMONGER
Would you like something to drink?

He indicates the drinks tray.

BERNIE
Well, actually Deirdre and I are pioneers.

Deirdre looks as though she might not be.

WHITTINGTON
I'm sure you are.

IMMONGER
She means they're teetotal.

WHITTINGTON
Ah. Tea perhaps?

BERNIE/DEIRDRE
(*together*)
That would be lovely./Great.

INT. STORMONT. DAY

Bernie and Deirdre, seated, facing Whittington and Immonger behind whom are the other heads.

DEIRDRE
The soldiers treat every man woman and child in Andersonstown as if we were all in the IRA.

Bernie has begun to rummage in her handbag.

BERNIE
The point is this, the IRA are willing to co-operate with us if you will.

WHITTINGTON
Have you spoken to the IRA?

BERNIE

Yes. They have conditions.

Still rummaging.

WHITTINGTON

Did they ask you to inform us of these conditions?

BERNIE

They did . . . Now I've got them here somewhere.

Everybody waits while she has a rummage.

DEIRDRE

I think I remember them.

Whittington and Immonger exchange glances.

BERNIE

Here we are. Oh, no, I have it now.

She takes out a long list and puts on her glasses.

One: a public declaration that the people of the thirty-two counties should decide the future of the country.

Close up on Whittington's weary face.

Two: withdrawal of all British Troops from Irish soil. Three: pending full withdrawal –

INT. STRANMILLIS FLAT. DAY

Annie is smoking, sitting on the bed, her shoes discarded, watching the door. The phone rings in the hallway. She runs out to answer it. She picks it up hopefully.

ANNIE

Hello?

FEMALE VOICE

Hello? . . . Is Owen there please? Can I speak to Owen?

ANNIE

Who's Owen?

FEMALE VOICE

I think I must have got the wrong number.

The phone goes dead.

INT. STORMONT. DAY

An even gloomier Whittington has finished listening to Bernie.

WHITTINGTON

I had hoped we were going to hear something new.

BERNIE

Who's fault is that? We're not politicians.

IMMONGER

But you're not just a spokesman for the IRA, are you?

DEIRDRE

We just want peace.

BERNIE
(*gasps*)

There was one more thing. They're going to call a ceasefire.

WHITTINGTON

The IRA are going to call a ceasefire?

BERNIE/DEIRDRE
(*together*)

Yes.

WHITTINGTON

Is that the message?

BERNIE

Yes. If you meet their conditions.

WHITTINGTON

This is not a serious proposal. They don't mean it.

BERNIE

Do they not?

WHITTINGTON

These demands go much further than anything they have asked for before.

IMMONGER

Do you have any ideas of your own of how we can go forward?

BERNIE

You could start by stopping the raids of innocent homes.

IMMONGER

How do you know they are innocent?

BERNIE

Sean Morris lives opposite me. He was lifted. And he's not involved in anything!

IMMONGER

But how do you know that?

BERNIE

He's a quiet wee man with a handicapped daughter. He's no time for politics.

DEIRDRE

You're talking about a very small group of people who are gunmen. The vast majority are not involved.

BERNIE

You keep raiding the houses of innocent people you'll drive the youth into the IRA.

WHITTINGTON

I'm sure we could look into the case – perhaps you'd let Jeremy have the details.

BERNIE

Certainly.

IMMONGER

And any others that you might know of.

INT. STRANMILLIS FLAT. DAY

It has begun to rain very heavily. A thunderstorm. The room is very very dark. Sound of a vacuum cleaner somewhere in the house.

A key turns in the lock; Annie is seated in a chair facing the door.

A female Cleaner looks in, dragging a vacuum behind her.

CLEANER

Can I clean this room now?

ANNIE

Yes.

The door is open wide. The woman vacuums.

Annie stares at the open door, then the rain running down the windows, then the clock: it's 6.30. She gets up and walks out of the room.

INT. STORMONT. DAY

The tea table has been laid out on a vast expanse of white cloth.

The party is now standing; Bernie and Deirdre on either side of Whittington.

IMMONGER

Those were the days . . . More tea?

Bernie and Deirdre hold out cups to be filled.

BERNIE/DEIRDRE
(*together*)

Yes please.

IMMONGER

Two for the price of one.

WHITTINGTON

My real interest is in you – and what the Peace Campaign will
do to influence the IRA?

BERNIE

We were thinking of going to the people of the estate.

DEIRDRE

We were thinking about a petition.

IMMONGER

A petition?

DEIRDRE

Yes.

IMMONGER

A petition. Yes, that's a good idea. A petition. That might be
just the sort of think one would need. What do you think, sir?

WHITTINGTON

I think that would be absolutely splendid. Absolutely
splendid.

INT. 139 MUCKROSS GARDENS. LIVING-ROOM. DAY

*Aidan is confronting Annie who is standing impassive and dripping wet
on the carpet.*

AIDAN

Where were you?

ANNIE

I was following the signs.

AIDAN

What signs?

ANNIE

Give way, no entry. Stop.

Aidan sighs.

AIDAN

Away and get changed or you'll catch your death.

EXT. DOORSTEP MONTAGE: ANDERSONSTOWN. MORNING/DAY/
EVENING

Doorstep No. 1: Bernie standing on Mrs Gilroy's doorstep with Deirdre.

MRS GILROY

My husband wouldn't let me.

Door slam.

Doorstep No. 2: door slam.

Doorstep No. 3: door slam.

Doorstep No. 4: door slam.

*Doorstep No. 5: Maureen and her Mother, Mrs Duffy, facing Bernie
and Deirdre.*

MRS DUFFY

Bernie – don't ask me. Our Roy works with Protestants.

BERNIE

What's that got to do with it?

MRS DUFFY

I don't want to get involved.

BERNIE

But we won't get peace if you don't get involved, May.

MRS DUFFY

I'll sign if I can remain anonymous.

Door closes.

Doorstep No. 6: door slam.

Doorstep No. 7: door slam.

Doorstep No. 8: Mrs Morris is at her front door with her daughter, facing Bernie.

MRS MORRIS

Of course I'll sign, Bernie. But I can't go around the doors collecting signatures.

BERNIE

That's all right, Sadie. We're collecting at the doors of the church as well. I wondered if –

MRS MORRIS

No. I can't do that, Bernie.

Doorstep No. 9: Bernie and Deirdre walking away from a closed door in a dilapidated street.

DEIRDRE

I think we're wasting our time! Should we give up?

BERNIE

No. Mary McCoy didn't have the choice.

EXT. MILLTOWN CEMETERY. DAY

Bernie standing at Mary McCoy's grave with a bunch of tiger lilies.

BERNIE
(*voice-over*)

Oh, Mary, I need a small miracle.

Out back to reveal the stone angels and Celtic crosses.

INT. CBS. GRAMMAR SCHOOL HALL. PRIZE DAY. MORNING

Bernie is facing an audience in the school hall: schoolboys on one side,

parents on the other. Deirdre is in the audience and Thomas and Brendan. Several of the Christian Brothers are behind Bernie.

BERNIE

I'd like to thank Brother Damien for allowing me to speak to you on this Prize Day. I'm speaking as a parent. I have two children at this school. I'm very proud of my children. I'm not very proud of myself.

CUT TO: *Thomas – who is groaning inwardly.*

And I know looking at the prizes spread out in front of me that you must be very proud of your children. But you ought to be ashamed of yourselves. Because we've failed this generation.

CUT TO: *Thomas and Brendan, who are looking physically sick.*

The rest of the audience looks stunned.

Every time a soldier is shot we keep quiet. Every time a civilian is shot we condemn the security forces. We're so predictable. I'd like to see a real change: I'd like to see us have the humanity to criticize the shooting of a soldier. I'd like to see the Army show real regret over the shooting of civilians. You have a chance to make the first move. On your way out of here today you can either stop and sign the peace petition – or pass by and fail another generation.

Bernie gets down from the platform and walks out of the hall in total silence.

EXT. CBS. BACK FIELD. DAY

A blank Women for Peace petition form fills the frame. A hand signs.

PULL BACK TO REVEAL *Bernie, Kathleen, Deirdre and Nora sitting at a long table at the end of the gorse-fringed playing fields. Four long queues of parents line up to sign at the table.*

NEWSPAPER MONTAGE

Belfast Telegraph *headline:* 'THE MCPHELIMY PRINCIPLES'

Belfast Telegraph *headline and photo:* 'BERNIE THE VISIONARY'

Fortnight, *picture with headline:* 'WHY BERNIE IS BIG IN BELFAST'

INT. RADIO STUDIO. DAY

Bernie is being interviewed in a BBC Radio studio by a local celebrity interviewer:

> BERNIE
>
> We've collected twenty-five thousand signatures in ten days.

> SUE
>
> That's a phenomenal turnout, but you did encounter some hostility at the beginning –

> BERNIE
>
> Och well, Sue, that's just grist to the mill: the more hostility I encounter the more determined I become.

> SUE
>
> But you actually changed people's attitudes, how did you do that?

BERNIE

I have tremendous energy and I'm a fighter. And I do know one big thing: you don't get peace without a fight.

CUT TO:

Of course, fame is very strange – absolute strangers think they know you. But I've got my feet firmly on the ground. Not everyone can handle that.

CUT TO:

I think everybody has a time when they come into their own. I just think this is my time.

SUE

Oh, so do you have any political ambitions?

BERNIE
(*laughs*)

Oh, none at all. Anyway I'm too old.

SUE

You don't look very old.

BERNIE

That's because I don't drink or smoke. And I need very little sleep.

SUE

The indomitable Mrs McPhelimy.

EXT. BACKDOOR. MUCKROSS. DAY

Annie is reading Thomas Hardy at the dinette table; Brendan is with her. Sinead opens the door from the living-room.

SINEAD

They're here.

INT. DINETTE DOOR TO LIVING-ROOM. DAY

Sinead opens the door wide. The room is full of men.

Cahir, Finbar, Tony and Aidan, with Bernie.

TONY

Right. Well, we'd better get this thing sorted.

FINBAR

Aye. We're a bit worried about this petition.

Thomas suddenly opens the back door and walks quickly through the dinette into the living-room.

THOMAS

Daddy. Naill French is gettin' ready to throw stones at the Army and um – there's a Saracen coming.

The Saracen thunders into view of the picture window. Followed by a hail of stones. Everyone rising to face the window.

BERNIE

Here we go again.

TONY

You might be taking a bit of a risk hanging around.

AIDAN

You should get out while you can.

FINBAR

We'll let you know if there's any need to make a move.

Three rapid knocks.

They all jump.

CAHIR

That'll be Owen.

BERNIE

Who's Owen?

Annie goes to get the door.

INT. HALL. MUCKROSS. DAY

Annie opens the door and comes face to face with Dino.

Dino/Owen walks past Annie into the living-room.

INT. LIVING-ROOM. DAY

Annie is standing right next to Dino/Owen, staring at him. Only Tony notices.

DINO/OWEN

We'll have to go now, sir. The Army's all over the place. We'll be lucky to get out of here at all.

He looks different; he's not wearing glasses. She is beginning to doubt her own sanity.

Aidan's POV: an Army personnel carrier arrives, dead-brakes up the road, Soldiers spew out, running towards the McPhelimys' and the stone-throwers.

Aidan turns from the window and collapses; blood pouring from his mouth.

BERNIE

Oh holy God! Aidan.

She falls down on top of him.

CAHIR

He's been shot!

TONY

No. He hasn't. It's his ulcer. Thomas, phone for an ambulance.

Thomas exits.

Dino/Owen moves to the window to watch: Soldiers have retreated from the Murrays' garden. The stone-throwers have melted away.

The Soldiers, in full riot gear, have formed a ring around two armoured cars.

Tony has moved to behind the hall door.

TONY
(*to Dino/Owen*)

I don't think there's any significance in this, it's where they usually stop.

Finbar and Cahir are clustered with Bernie around Aidan.

Annie is staring at her father and the cool Dino/Owen and considering having hysterics.

Brendan has vanished.

> FINBAR
>
> Maybe if we sat him up.

> CAHIR
>
> Okay, you take his other arm.

They haul Aidan up and a fresh stream of blood spurts out, causing him to choke.

> BERNIE
>
> Oh, for God's sake, somebody help him. Do something.

> FINBAR
>
> Can you help us here, Owen?

Dino/Owen steps away from the window and picks up a small cushion.

> DINO/OWEN
>
> Here. Keep his airways clear.

He places a pillow under Aidan's head and steps back to the window.

> FINBAR
>
> Owen's a medical student. You're in good hands.

> DINO/OWEN
>
> Make sure he can breathe at all times.

Annie begins to have hysterics; Sinead watches calmly.

> BERNIE
>
> Ah holy mother of God don't you go tripping out on me now, girl. Get a hold of yourself, Annie!

> AIDAN
> (*opening his eyes*)
>
> I told you – you shouldn't be here.

Thomas enters.

THOMAS

The ambulance is on its way.

BERNIE

It'll never get through. The roads are all blocked. There's two burnt-out buses at the Christian Brothers. Oh Christ, what'll we do?

FINBAR

We'll take you to hospital ourselves, Mrs McPhelimy, if the ambulance isn't here in a few minutes.

Dino/Owen walks rapidly through the living-room to check the kitchen exit. He looks through the dinette window to the long exposed back garden.

AIDAN

No, Ciarin. Get out now. Right away.

Dino/Owen comes back.

Tony! Get over the back fence. You'll be in Desy Martin's back garden. Go through the house. Desy'll help you. Go on, Ciarin.

DINO/OWEN

He's right. It's time you were gone.

FINBAR/CIARIN

No.

CAHIR

Should we get him on to the sofa?

TONY

I think we'd better leave him where he is.

A knock at the door of biblical proportions.

THOMAS

Oh fuck, it's the Army.

Finbar/Ciarin looks towards the kitchen exit, and then at Aidan's face. He is resigned, drops his head.

Brendan dashes in through the back door.

96

BRENDAN

It's the ambulance men.

TONY

Right. Thomas, you get the door. We're leaving now. Come on, Ciarin!

Tony leads Finbar/Ciarin and Cahir through the kitchen, followed by Dino/Owen.

Thomas opens the front door.

Bernie gets up.

The back door closes as two Ambulance Men enter the living-room with a stretcher.

Annie looks through the dinette door/window down the long garden to the retreating men and Dino/Owen.

Two Soldiers follow the Ambulance Men into the living-room to help with the stretcher.

Annie shuts the dinette door quietly.

THOMAS
(off)

It's his ulcer. It's bleeding again.

DRIVER
(off)

139 Muckross? Again! They'll be putting an accident black spot at your front door.

Annie opens the door again and steps into the kitchen; she looks down the empty garden.

She turns to the side, Dino/Owen is standing in the kitchen.

DINO/OWEN

From the moment your mother got involved with the Peace Women the intelligence services had your whole family under surveillance . . . That day in the rain . . . they were watching the flat . . . Say something.

Annie shakes her head.

97

Fine . . . Bye . . .

He walks out and disappears down the garden.

EXT. MUCKROSS GARDENS. DAY

Brendan and Thomas watch the ambulance leave.

> BRENDAN
>
> M'daddy knew that man. He called him Ciarin.

> THOMAS
>
> Aye.

> BRENDAN
>
> So the story's true.

> THOMAS
>
> What story's that?

> BRENDAN
>
> M'da was in the IRA and ma made him leave it or she wouldn't marry him.

> THOMAS
>
> I won't. I won't tell anyone that Finbar's real name is Ciarin.

INT. HALL. NIGHT

Annie is sitting at the bottom of the stairs, when the front door opens. Bernie comes back from the hospital.

> BERNIE
>
> Why aren't you in bed?

> ANNIE
>
> Because I wanted you to know that you have ruined our lives through your overwheening vanity. And I hate you.

> BERNIE
>
> Have you taken something?

> ANNIE
>
> Yes. I have swallowed the rest of the Valium in your bottle.

Bernie cries out.

I also want you to know that I'm counting the days 'til I can leave you.

Bernie grabs her.

> ### BERNIE
>
> Out! Get out! Walk!

EXT. MUCKROSS GARDENS. NIGHT

Bernie is walking Annie up and down the street in the dark.

A Soldier lying behind the hedge raises his head as they pass, and then lowers it again.

> ### ANNIE
>
> You don't want peace, mother. You just want the publicity.

> ### BERNIE
>
> You're a stupid, stupid girl.

> ### ANNIE
>
> Do you have any idea what your attention-seeking behaviour has meant to the rest of us?

> ### BERNIE
>
> How many did you take? Six or ten?

> ### ANNIE
>
> You've destroyed us. You've killed your family. You're the stupid one!

Bernie stares at her daughter.

> ### BERNIE
>
> My God! How dare you make me responsible.

> ### ANNIE
>
> You are responsible, you cow! Do you know Sinead cries herself to sleep every night over you. Do you know that Brother Damien lets Brendan and Thomas leave school twenty minutes before the bell – in case they don't get to the front gate in one piece. And me? Mother, I'll never forgive what you did to me!

BERNIE

No more!

They have come parallel with a hedgerow where several members of a footpatrol are watching with blackened faces.

Annie suddenly retches. Straightens up and wipes her mouth.

ANNIE

There is no more, mother.

Annie turns and walks back to the house.

Bernie, finding herself alone, comes face to face with the disguised footpatrol.

PATROL LEADER

Nice night.

Bernie turns and walks back to the house.

INT. STORMONT. CORRIDOR. DAY

A small procession rushes along the corridor, led by Whittington and Bernie, past gilt-framed ex-Ministers, followed by Deirdre and Immonger.

WHITTINGTON

Marvellous. What a triumph for you.

BERNIE

Aye. It is. We wrung those signatures out of the people in Andersonstown, Mr Whittington.

WHITTINGTON

Have you ever considered a career in politics, Mrs McPhelimy?

Bernie stops.

BERNIE

I won't even have a life, Mr Whittington, if you don't keep your part of the bargain.

WHITTINGTON

Please, call me George.

BERNIE

The house raids are still continuing!

WHITTINGTON

I promise you, Mrs McPhelimy, we are dealing with that.

IMMONGER

You will appreciate that it takes a little while for our
information to filter through to forces on the ground.

BERNIE

What are you talking about? What information? I want the
raids to stop for everyone – not just the people who signed the
petition.

EXT. STORMONT. ENTRANCE STEPS. DAY

*Cameras flashing. Smiles, handshakes, applause: Deirdre hands over
the petition to Whittington.*

DEIRDRE

We wish to thank the people of Andersonstown for having the
courage to stand up and be counted among the peacemakers.
I'm delighted to be able to hand this over to em . . . sorry –
the Paramilitary Secretary of State for Northern Ireland, as an
expression of the desire of the Catholic people of West Belfast
for peace.

A gang of Reporters turn on Bernie.

MALE REPORTER

Does this petition mean that the majority of people in
Andersonstown do not support the IRA?

BERNIE

No comment.

MALE REPORTER

But, Mrs McPhelimy – if the majority want peace they don't
want the IRA. Isn't that so?

BERNIE

Are you remedial or just deaf? I said no comment.

Immonger approaches the press:

IMMONGER
I think that's enough for now, gentlemen. The Secretary for State will be making a statement in due course. Thank you.

Returning to the Parliament building:

BERNIE
We're doing your job for you, Mr Whittington.

WHITTINGTON
You've done very well. Very well indeed.

Whittington is smiling. Bernie isn't.

EXT. NEWSPAPER HEADLINE. DAY

A bundle of tied-up newspapers are dropped displaying the headline and photo for the Irish Independent: 'BERNIE TOPS THE READERS POLL'.

INT. MUCKROSS GARDENS. TONY'S CAR. LATER

Tony is helping Aidan along the path from his car.

Bernie opens the door.

Aidan looks grimly at her.

Tony doesn't speak.

On the path Bernie fetches Aidan's things from Tony.

> BERNIE
> Tony, I'll take that.

He goes back to his car, leaving Aidan and Bernie.

> It was nice of Tony to drive you home.

> AIDAN
> I asked him to.

> BERNIE
> Mr Morris is out.

> AIDAN
> No doubt they rushed over to thank you.

Aidan walks past her into the house; and Bernie stands looking across at Morris's shut door.

INT. KITCHEN. CONTINUOUS TIME. DAY

Bernie follows Aidan into the kitchen.

> BERNIE
> Aidan, why are you so angry with me?

> AIDAN
> I'm not angry *with* you – I'm angry *for* you, love. I think you're being given the run-around.

> BERNIE
> No. I like Whittington. I think he's genuine.

> AIDAN
> I wasn't just talking about Whittington.

EXT. ANDERSONSTOWN ROAD. NIGHT

Bernie is walking past a high hedge; end sounds of an evening bell tolling.

A Youth in a balaclava thrusts her into the hedge while another Youth keeps watch.

Bernie cries out.

A gun is pressed to her temple.

> REPUBLICAN YOUTH
>
> Do you know what I'm going to do to you? I am going to put a bullet in your head. And then I'm going to string your body up on the lamppost outside your house for your kids to find in the morning . . . You'll not make any more phone calls to Jeremy. You'll not drink any more cups of tea with George . . . You're a dead bitch.

He shoves her further against the hedge; she cries out again.

Then both Youths run away.

INT. CHAPEL. NIGHT

Father Clancy is listening at the grill of a confession box.

> BERNIE
>
> I don't know if I'm going to make it home tonight. You may be the last person to see me or speak to me.

Bernie breaks down.

> CLANCY
>
> Bernie. Tell me what has happened?

> BERNIE
>
> Someone has just threatened to shoot me and hang my body up outside the house for the kids to find. Will you promise me that you'll not let the kids find me like that. You'll cut me down?

> CLANCY
>
> This is too serious. Let's get out of here. We'll go next door to my house and ring Aidan.

No! Aidan's not to know. You can't tell anyone what I've told you. I'm in confession. But if I am shot, I want your promise that you will preach that sermon that I'm a peacemaker not an informer.

CLANCY

I promise.

BERNIE

And you won't let the kids see me like that? You'll cut me down? After I'm dead. You'll cut my body down?

CLANCY

I will.

EXT. CHURCH DOOR. NIGHT

Bernie passes the high hedge. Another set of double footsteps are pursuing her. She walks on quickly. The other footsteps begin to run, then they pass her by. She stops, looking at the departing shadowy figures of two Young Men hurrying past.

INT. MUCKROSS. BEDROOM. NIGHT

In bed, Bernie is crying. Aidan, who has his back to her, turns:

AIDAN

Och, love, what's wrong?

He puts his arms around her.

VOICES
(*off*)

Touts out! Out! Out! Out!

EXT. MUCKROSS GARDENS. NIGHT

A huge loudly jeering crowd has gathered, including recognizable people from the neighbourhood, like the Frenchs and the Murrays. Brigitte is there.

Aidan opens the front door and charges out with the ornamental sword from the hall.

MOB

Traitors! Out! Out! Out!

AIDAN

Take yourselves off! Stand back! Don't make me use this!

MOB

Peace with justice! Sell out! Touts out! Touts out!

Thomas appears at Aidan's side with a hurley stick.

Bernie and Annie appear. Bernie is carrying a broom.

Annie steps out.

ANNIE

Brigitte?

BRIGITTE

Out! Out! Out!

Annie backs away; Bernie grabs her.

BERNIE

Run around and get Tony! Tell him what's happening.

ANNIE

I'm not leaving.

BERNIE
(*giving her a push*)
Go on, we're depending on you.

Annie slips away across the Murrays' garden and begins to run.

Then she stops – and turns and runs in the opposite direction as if she has forgotten.

MRS BRENNAN

You forged those signatures.

BERNIE

That's nonsense and you know it.

FRENCH

Oh yeah. Well, I don't know anybody who signed. Do yous?
(*appealing to the mob*)

I only know one woman who's signed – but God love her, she's not all there.

Jeering laughter.

The Mob are circling Bernie, Aidan and Thomas.

Who do you think you are anyway?

MRS BRENNAN

Who gave you the right to speak for us?

FRENCH

How much are they paying you?

Bernie makes a lunge with the broom.

Aidan pulls her back.

EXT. STREETS. NIGHT

Annie's night run through the streets, alleys and gardens.

EXT. CASEMENT PARK. NIGHT

Annie is fast approaching the house where Dino collected his laundry.

She reaches the front door, hammers with the stout knocker.

The house looks asleep, closed up.

She stands back and calls up to the first-floor window.

> ANNIE
>
> Dino! Dino! Speak to me! Someone! Dino! Owen! Anybody!

Lights go on in the downstairs bay windows, then the hall, before the front door is open by a dark-haired young woman in a dressing-gown. Annie approaches the door.

> I need help.

> DINO
> (*off*)
>
> Who is it?

EXT. ANDERSONSTOWN STREETS. NIGHT

Dino and Annie are running back along the same route towards Muckross.

> ANNIE
>
> Why is peace such a dirty word!

> DINO
>
> We think the Brits are analysing the petition. And whoever isn't on it will be suspected of supporting terrorists.

> ANNIE
>
> I don't believe you!

> DINO
>
> It doesn't matter what you believe. That crowd outside your door believe it.

They have turned into Muckross Gardens.

> ANNIE
>
> Oh my God! They're in the house.

They race towards the house.

EXT. MUCKROSS GARDENS. NIGHT

*The Mob have invaded the house and furniture is being removed.
Aidan and Thomas are struggling to hold on to a chair in the front
garden.*

Annie pushes through the crowd towards them.

*Annie reaches Thomas's side as a hatchet comes down – he turns and
catches it in the ear.*

> ANNIE
>
> Daddy!

Thomas collapses at her feet and rolls slightly.

The Mob disperse to avoid the fall-out; and Dino plunges towards them.

Everything goes completely still.

*Bernie comes out of the house; she finds herself looking into the cut lip of
Thomas's head.*

*Bernie drops to her knees beside Thomas and gathers him up – it is like
a scene from the* pièta.

> BERNIE
>
> What have you done! What have you done to my son?

Annie screams and rushes at the crowd.

> ANNIE
>
> You fucking bastarding morons! I damn everyone of you to
> hell. I swear to God you'll rue the day you opened my
> brother's head!

She turns towards French and Brigitte.

> And you, you evil oul whore! I curse you and your whole
> fucking family to the devil. May you never –

Dino grabs her.

Aidan is helplessly looking at Thomas.

> AIDAN
>
> Jesus, Bernie. Jesus.

A car screeches to a halt.

Tony arrives with three men.

Doors slamming.

They all get out and stand behind Dino.

The Mob begins to retreat.

> TONY

Don't try anything like this again. Go on!

Dino kneels to examine Thomas.

> ANNIE

Get a doctor!

> BERNIE

I thought you were supposed to be a doctor?

> ANNIE

Not him. We need a real doctor!

Three armed Men are on guard; the Mob have evaporated. Tony comes to help.

> TONY

What happened?

> DINO
> (*to Aidan*)

You need to get him to the hospital. Are you fit to drive?

> AIDAN

I am. Yes. I am.

> TONY

Take my car.

INT. CAR. NIGHT

The car is driven at speed by Aidan.

Bernie is holding Thomas's head to her breast.

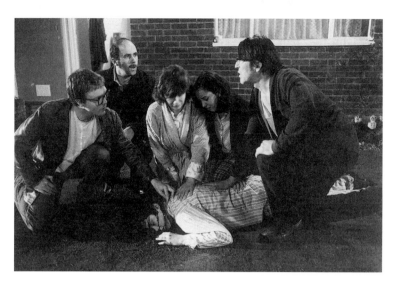

Marymotheragod, Marymotheragod.

Annie in the back with Bernie.

INT. CHILDREN'S WARD. NIGHT

Only a few beds occupied.

The Night Nurse is on duty at the far end of the ward with a lamp over her desk.

Bernie and Annie sit on either side of Thomas's bed. He is unconscious and wearing a turban bandage.

Bernie stares bleakly.

BERNIE
If anything happens to this child, I will lose my mind.

Bernie watches over Thomas.

Annie is fearful she may have already lost her mind.

ANNIE
I'll never forgive them.

BERNIE

Don't say that. If you say that he won't get better.

ANNIE

You can forgive them. I won't.

BERNIE

If you don't forgive them, you can't forgive me.

ANNIE

I do. I do.

BERNIE

The only thing I can be proud of – my children aren't full of hate. Promise me you'll forgive them now! Promise me.

ANNIE

I do. I do. I forgive them. I do.

BERNIE

Forgive me.

ANNIE

I do.

The Night Nurse approaches.

NIGHT NURSE

Mrs McPhelimy. Do you want a sedative?

Bernie shakes her head.

BERNIE

I want to pull the curtains round.

NIGHT NURSE

I can't let you do that.

BERNIE

Does everyone have to see us like this?

NIGHT NURSE

I won't be able to see the other children's beds.

Bernie slumps down, defeated. Annie sits down on the opposite side of the bed.

The Night Nurse withdraws to her lamplit desk.

INT. GYM HALL. EXAM ROOM. MORNING

CUT TO: *clock face in the school gym which reads 9.15 a.m.*

Sister Aloysius looks at the faces of the waiting uniformed Schoolgirls. Maureen looks particularly alarmed; she looks hopefully to the door. Miss Savage is standing beneath the clock. Maureen gets up and approaches her.

INT. HOSPITAL. ACCIDENT AND EMERGENCY WAITING AREA. MORNING

Annie, Bernie, Deirdre and Miss Savage, who has come to the hospital.

                    ANNIE
It's just an exam.

                    MISS SAVAGE
For which you've worked very hard.

                    BERNIE
She's in no fit state. Can she not do it another time?

                    MISS SAVAGE
They'd make her wait 'til next year.

                    DEIRDRE
I think she should go, Bernie.

                    BERNIE
I don't mind what she does.

                    ANNIE
Is that true?

                    BERNIE
Oh for Christ's sake why is everybody making me responsible for everything that happens! Do the exam because you want to do it or don't! It's nothing to do with me!

Annie is staring in bewilderment at Bernie.

113

INT. SCHOOL GYM/EXAM CENTRE. MORNING

Sister Aloysius is invigilating.

Miss Savage leads Annie to her desk.

One hundred heads lift off their pages.

Maureen looks worried; Annie has passed by unseeing.

Annie sits shakily.

Everyone is staring; she recognizes various faces of hostility, in particular Brigitte who is directly across the aisle from her.

Annie looks at the exam paper on her desk.

> ANNIE
> I haven't got a pen.

She begins to look around for Maureen but still doesn't see her.

Her distress becomes plain as various heads turn to look in her direction.

> Can anyone lend me a pen?

She stares helplessly at the page.

Brigitte gets up and walks towards her holding out a pen.

INT. ANNIE'S BEDROOM. DAY. NIGHT

Annie is packing: there are several cardboard boxes taped up and named. She clears all the foreign dolls from her shelf and puts them into a cardboard box on which she writes the word 'Sinead'. Into an 'Annie' box she drops her poetry books.

Bernie opens the bedroom door.

> BERNIE
> Tony got lifted by the Army last night. Your daddy thinks it's my fault.

> ANNIE
> You have to do what you think is right.

BERNIE

Even his sisters in Australia know about it. They wrote him a letter but he wouldn't show it to me.

ANNIE

Who gives a shite what they think.

BERNIE

It's all right them living in Melbourne giving money to the Provos to keep the home fires burning, while they live in peace.

Bernie sits down on the bed, sighs, overwhelmed suddenly by suffering.

Och, Mary dear . . . I should have gone with her, you know, to the St Patrick's Day Parade in New York.

ANNIE

Who are you talking about?

BERNIE

Mary McCoy. Every year she went. And every year she asked me to go with her.

ANNIE

I don't think you'd be very welcome there, mother.

BERNIE

No. I'm not exactly lucky for people, am I? Tony says that young fella who helped us that night was lifted as well. The medical student. What was his name?

ANNIE

I don't remember his name.

BERNIE

Owen. It was Owen.

INT. LONG KESH. PRISON CAMP. DAY

Annie sits opposite Dino at the prison camp.

DINO

What's it like out?

115

ANNIE

It's raining.

DINO

Is it?

He leans forward to smell her.

I love the smell of rain.

ANNIE

What is your real name?

DINO

Dino.

ANNIE

Was I a cover?

DINO

You mustn't do that. Mix things together that don't go.

ANNIE

I mustn't do that!

DINO

Yes. You have to learn to separate things out. You were my girlfriend. You were my real girlfriend.

ANNIE

I was in love with you.

He stares at her sadly.

DINO

What? You think I shouldn't have got involved with you because I got involved with them.

ANNIE

You should've told me.

DINO

Like you told me about Bernie?

Pause.

Bernie is a very big person, she'll be all right you know. So will you.

ANNIE

Do you want me to wait?

He leans over.

No. Don't wait. Nobody should every wait – for anybody. Get out there, McPhelimy.

I have to go now.

DINO

Indeed you do.

Annie gets to her feet.

It's been nice talking to you.

ANNIE

The story about the chimes –

DINO

The ice-cream van.

ANNIE

Was that true?

DINO
(thinks for a minute)

Yes.

ANNIE

Good.

Dino looks at her admiringly.

See ya.

She walks away.

DINO
(quietly)

See ya.

117

EXT. MUCKROSS GARDENS. MORNING

*Patsy French is standing on her front lawn with Naill watching the
McPhelimys departure; Brendan is helping Aidan rearrange the contents
of the back of the van; Annie hands Thomas a box of books and returns
to the house.*

FRENCH

Did you ever hear the like of that wee girl's tongue!

NAILL

Do you want me to break in when they go – see if they've left
anything useful?

FRENCH

What? And get yourself kneecapped? Fucking stupid
bastarding moron . . . Wait until it's dark first.

INT. WINDOW. LIVING-ROOM. MORNING

*Annie and Bernie are standing in the empty living-room, where
everything has been stripped away and packed up. They are watching
Aidan and Thomas shift a piece of furniture into the van, while
Brendan supervises.*

ANNIE

Where we're moving to? Is it safe?

BERNIE

Safe? What's safe? Sure no one can hurt you like your own
. . . I resigned from the peace movement this morning.

ANNIE

Well, you started it. Let someone else take it up now.

BERNIE

I wasn't wrong, Annie. Because I was naive doesn't mean I
was wrong.

ANNIE

You weren't wrong.

BERNIE

I'm talking about the petition. I wasn't wrong to collect those
signatures. I would do it again. Even if I fail again.

ANNIE

You didn't fail us. We just didn't have your strength.

Looking out at Thomas and Aidan and Brendan struggling to lift the sofa on to the back of the van, Bernie realizes the enormity of what has happened.

BERNIE

Oh, look at my boys!

Bernie breaks down and cries.

I've hurt my boys and I never meant to.

Sinead comes in with a Spanish dancer.

SINEAD

Could you make me a dress like this? Why is mammy crying?

ANNIE

She's worried about the boys.

SINEAD

Yeah. I know.

All three look out of the living-room window at the other three outside at the van.

Can we go now?

ANNIE

Yeah . . .

(*suddenly Annie leans forward*)

Mammy, look!

Bernie's POV: The door of the Morris house opens and Mrs Morris appears. She walks to the van, her husband Sean, and daughter Bridie, behind her. She has a tray with tea and oranges for Aidan and the two Boys.

Then Sean Morris helps the Boys and Aidan lift the sofa on to the van. At the window Annie puts one arm around Bernie, and the other around Sinead.

                    BERNIE
                (very quietly)
God bless you, Mrs Morris.

EXT. 139 MUCKROSS GARDENS. LATER. DAY

Aidan shuts the front door, then stops.

Bernie waits for him.

                    AIDAN
I'll just go back in and check.

                    BERNIE
Don't go back in.

Aidan looks at his wife, nods.

                    AIDAN
Aye. You're right.

                    BERNIE
What do you think you forgot?

                    AIDAN
Makes no difference now anyway. I remembered you, didn't
I?

*He puts his arm around her. Bernie smiles gratefully at her husband.
Together they walk along the path.*

*Annie, Thomas, Brendan and Sinead are packed on to the back of the
van, waiting.*

Nora comes rushing up the street towards them.

                    AIDAN
There's Nora now.

                    BERNIE
I hope she hasn't brought me anything from the Kesh for I've
no room.

Nora arrives, puffing and panting.

NORA

Sorry I'm late.

BERNIE

How was Desy?

NORA

I didn't see him.

AIDAN

You didn't see him!

NORA

He's gone on the run.

AIDAN

What – he's escaped?

NORA

No, he's gone on the run in the prison.

They get into the van with the others, Aidan behind the wheel.

The van moves off.

AIDAN
(*voice-over*)

How do you go on the run in the prison?

NORA
(*voice-over*)

He sleeps out in different cells every night. They just haven't been able to find him.

BERNIE
(*voice-over*)

Isn't that our Desy all over.

The van passes by as:

A Man is mending his lawnmower in a front garden.

Someone is washing windows.

A Woman is pushing a pram.

A distant explosion is heard; followed by a plume of smoke.

Two Army vehicles trundle down the road at speed.

The Man's lawnmower splutters into life.

The Woman gives the baby in the pram a dropped toy.

The Window Cleaner continues washing a whole terrace of windows.

CAPTION:
>   These things happened twenty-five years ago.
>   Bernie McPhelimy still lives in West Belfast.

Credits

CAST

BERNIE MCPHELIMY	Julie Walters
AIDAN MCPHELIMY	Ciaran Hinds
ANNIE MCPHELIMY	Nuala O'Neill
THOMAS MCPHELIMY	James Loughran
BRENDAN MCPHELIMY	Barry Loughran
SINEAD MCPHELIMY	Elizabeth Donaghy
DINO/OWEN	Ciaran McMenamin
PATSY FRENCH	Jaz Pollock
NIALL FRENCH	Caolan Byrne
DEIRDRE	Aingeal Grehan
WHITTINGTON	Oliver Ford Davies
IMMONGER	Nicholas Woodeson
FINBAR/CIARIN	Des McAleer
NORA	Doreen Hepburn
KATHLEEN	Ruth McCabe
MARY MCCOY	Veronica Duffy
COLM	Timmy McCoy
TONY	Lorcan Cranitch
ROSALEEN	Cathy White
UNCLE JAMES	Malcolm Rogers
LUCY	Tracey Wilkinson
BRIDGET	Kelly Flynn
MAUREEN	Cheryl O'Dwyer
MRS MORRIS	Maggie Shevlin
GUNMAN	Billy Clarke
MISS SAVAGE	Fo Cullen
JIMMY CANE	Simon Fullerton
LIONEL THIRSTON	Duncan Marwick
SERGEANT	John Drummond
LANKY PARA	Paul Trussell

1ST PARA	Lee Nettleingham
2ND PARA	Neil Maskell
3RD PARA	Peter Ferdinando
4TH PARA	Mark Mooney
CORPORAL	Darren Bancroft
NUALA CURRAN	Claire Murphy
MRS GILROY	Julia Dearden
MAIREAD CURRAN	Mairead Redmond
OFFICER	Andrew Havill
MRS BRENNAN	Paula Hamilton
BUTCHER	Mike Dowling
BUS DRIVER	Robert Calvert
MRS LOCKHART	Jeananne Crowley
FERGUS	Peter Ballance
BRIAN	Richard Clements
INTERVIEWER	Colum Convey
NIGHT NURSE	Amanda Hurwitz
CORK DRIVER	Tony Rohr
CAHIR	B. J. Hogg
PATROL LEADER	Richard Smedley
REPORTER	Alan McKee
REBUBLICAN YOUTH	Tony Devlin
AMBULANCE DRIVER	Andrew Downs
PARAMEDIC	Breffni McKenna
PUBLICAN	John Quinn
HIJACK YOUTH	Packy Lee
TV JOURNALIST	Caitriona Hinds
1ST JOURNALIST	Christina Nelson
2ND JOURNALIST	Gerard McCartney
NURSE	Karen Staples
FATHER CLANCY	Kieran Ahern
MRS DUFFY	Brenda Winter
MAN IN BLACK JACKET	Richard Orr
1ST RADIO INTERVIEWER	Chris Parr
2ND RADIO INTERVIEWER	Fiona Shaw

CREW

Director	Roger Michell
Producers	George Faber
	Charles Pattinson
Executive Producers	David Thompson
	Robert Cooper
	Rainer Mockert
Screenplay from the novel by	
Mary Costello	Anne Devlin
Line Producer	Sally French
Music	Trevor Jones
Editor	Kate Evans
Director of Photography	John Daly
Production Designer	Pat Campbell
Art Director	Dave Arrowsmith
Costume Designer	Hazel Pethig
Casting Director	Sarah Trevis
Visual FX	John Markwell
Sound Mixer	Rosie Straker
Chief Make-up and Hair	Jean Speak
Stunt Co-ordinator	Andy Bradford
Production Co-ordinator	Winnie Wishart
Assistant Co-ordinator	Mel Claus
Trainee Co-ordinator	Julie Connor
Production Runner	Lorna Whittaker
1st Assistant Director	Deborah Saban
2nd Assistant Director	Olivia Lloyd
3rd Assistant Director	Lee Trevor
Floor Runner	Jojo Tulloch
Runner	Jasmine Cavendish
Runner (Belfast)	Rory McCadden
Script Supervisor	Kim Armitage
Location Manager	Sam Breckman
Locations (Belfast)	Michael Casey
Locations Assistant (London)	Duncan Muggoch
Production Accountant	Trevor Stanley
Assistant Accountant	Rachel Smith
Casting (Belfast)	Hilary Hannah
Voice Coach	Joan Washington
Focus Puller	Steve Wallace
Clapper/Loader	Paul Lang

125

Grip	Gary Hymns
Camera Trainee	Andrew Gardner
Sound Maintenance	Martin Beresford
Sound Trainee	Jennifer Woods
Gaffer	Dick Reed
Best Boy	Laurie Dodson
Assistant Art Director	Emma MacDevitt
Production Buyer	Hazel Storey
Art Department Assistant	Muffin Green
Art Department Runner	Paul Munford
Props Master	Bob Orr
Dressing Props	John Booth
	Dennis Knotts
Stand-by Props	Tristan Carlisle Kitz
	Bill Gower
Storeman	Mickey Powell
Props Pickup Driver	Graham Gordon
Construction Manager	Colin Fraser
Chargehand	Derek Fraser
Carpenters	Muir Balfour
	Brian Adams
	Tommy Dowdals
	Mark Harrod
	Neil Querns
Stand-by Carpenter	John Watt
Chargehand Painter	Jim Patrick
Painters	Bobby Gee
	Terry Weaver
Stand-by Rigger	Drew Meldon
Stagehands	Brian Boyne
	John Donnelly
Labourer	David Roy
Asst Costume Designer	Leah Archer
Costume Assistant	Sue Mewton
Costume Trainee	Sarah Kelly
Hair/Make-Up Artist	Kay Bilk
Stills Photography	Millie Donaghy
	Liam Daniel
Publicity	Corbett & Keene
Catering (London)	Andy Aldridge
Catering (Belfast)	Route Catering
Military Advisor	Richard Smedley

Action Vehicles   David Sutcliffe
Unit Driver   Jeff Oldman

A COMPANY PICTURES PRODUCTION FOR PANDORA CINEMA,
BBC FILMS, BRITISH SCREEN AND THE ARTS COUNCIL OF
NORTHERN IRELAND'S NATIONAL LOTTERY FUND